**FUNDAMENTALS
OF
BOTANY
SERIES**

VASCULAR

PLANTS: FORM

AND FUNCTION

FUNDAMENTALS
OF
BOTANY
SERIES

edited by
WILLIAM A. JENSEN,
University of California
LEROY G. KAVALJIAN,
Sacramento State College

THE PLANT CELL
William A. Jensen, University of California

REPRODUCTION, HEREDITY, AND SEXUALITY
Stanton A. Cook, University of Oregon

NONVASCULAR PLANTS: FORM AND FUNCTION
William T. Doyle, Northwestern University

VASCULAR PLANTS: FORM AND FUNCTION
Frank B. Salisbury and Robert V. Parke, Colorado State University

PLANTS AND THE ECOSYSTEM
W. D. Billings, Duke University

EVOLUTION AND PLANTS OF THE PAST
Harlan C. Banks, Cornell University

PLANTS AND CIVILIZATION
Herbert G. Baker, University of California

PHOTOLITHOPRINTED BY MALLOY LITHOGRAPHING, INC.
ANN ARBOR, MICHIGAN

Frank B. Salisbury

Robert V. Parke

COLORADO STATE UNIVERSITY

VASCULAR

PLANTS: FORM

AND FUNCTION

WADSWORTH PUBLISHING COMPANY, INC.
Belmont, California

Third printing: July 1965

L.C. Cat. Card No.: 64–23904

Printed in the United States of America

FOREWORD

Because of the immensity and complexity of the field of botany, the great diversity of plants, and the many methods of plant study, the problem of how to present to the student the highlights of botanical knowledge gained over centuries is not easy to solve. The authors and editors of the volumes in this series believe that an understanding of plants—their parts, their activities, and their relationship to man—is of fundamental importance in appreciating the significance of life. To stress this concept, the form and function of plants, tissues, and cells are treated together. At all levels of organization, in each volume, information gathered by morphologists, physiologists, cytologists, taxonomists, geneticists, biochemists, and ecologists is combined.

Thus, in the volume on *The Plant Cell* by William A. Jensen, the structure and function of the various cell parts are discussed together —for example, mitochondria and respiration, photosynthesis and chloroplasts. The volume by Stanton A. Cook, *Reproduction, Heredity, and Sexuality,* combines the principles of genetics with the means of reproduction in the various plant groups. *Nonvascular Plants: Form and Function,* by William T. Doyle, and *Vascular Plants: Form and Function,* by Frank B. Salisbury and Robert V. Parke, cover the major plant groups and discuss the plants in terms of morphology, physiology, and biochemistry. The relation of plants, particularly vascular plants, to their environment and to each other is covered in *Plants and the Ecosystem* by W. D. Billings. The form and distribution of plants of the past and their relation to the concepts of evolution are considered by Harlan Banks in *Evolution and Plants of the Past.* Herbert G. Baker, in *Plants and Civilization,* discusses the importance of plants to man's social and economic development and the equally important consideration of man's role in the modification and distribution of plants.

In a series such as this, the editors are faced with the task of dividing a broad field into areas that can be presented in a meaningful way by the authors. There must be logic in the entire scheme, with few gaps and a minimum of overlap. Yet an instructor may not want to use the series of volumes in the sequence and manner preferred by the editors. Consequently, each volume must be usable alone and also in any sequence with the others. To achieve such a high degree of versatility is difficult, but we believe the series exhibits these features.

A concerted effort has been made by the authors and editors to maintain a consistent level of presentation. However, each author has been encouraged to approach his subject in his own way and to write in his own style in order to provide variety and to exploit the uniqueness of the individual author's viewpoint. Finally, while presenting the principles of botany we have tried to communicate the excitement of recent developments as well as the joy that comes with the extension of knowledge in any field.

The topic of this volume is the functioning plant itself. After a brief survey of the different kinds of vascular plants, the text outlines current knowledge of higher plant structure and development. Following each discussion of anatomy is a consideration of the manner in which the organ under discussion functions. A great deal of such activity occurs on the biochemical level, and such topics are presented in detail in Jensen: *The Plant Cell*. This volume first considers functions relating to movement of water and dissolved substances within the plant, and then emphasizes the broad function of growth, which is often a response to environmental change. Perhaps at present the most fruitful area of biological research is at the cellular level, but surely a beckoning frontier is that of growth at the organ level. Present efforts in this field—studies on plant hormones and other growth substances, experimental morphology, morphogenetic responses to light, and biological time measurement—might help point the way to the future. This volume surveys some of the most recent advances and indicates some of the potentials in this complex and dynamic branch of plant science.

CONTENTS

1

THE VASCULAR
PLANTS

The plants discussed in this volume are all members of the division referred to as vascular plants (Tracheophyta), and the purpose of this chapter is to survey briefly the general kinds of plants within this group and to place in proper perspective the discussions of anatomical features and physiological activities that follow. No attempt will be made to consider these aspects in relation to all the vascular plants, but we will emphasize those groups that are most commonly encountered, that have the greatest number of species, and that have been most thoroughly studied (dicotyledons, monocotyledons, and gymnosperms, in that order).

THE CLASSIFICATION OF PLANTS

An important field of botanical endeavor during the past three centuries has been the classification (organizing or arranging) of plants into logical groups. Some systems are artificial (such as a division into trees, shrubs, and herbs), but the aim of taxonomists (specialists in classification) has been to develop a system that reflects the natural (evolutionary) relationships among plants.

The basic unit or *taxon* of classification is the *species,* although no completely acceptable definition of the species has yet been put forth. Species are grouped into *genera,* and the *scientific name* of a given plant consists of the genus name and species name. The roots of this double name are basically Latin, although words from many other languages are often used and Latinized. The scientific name of a plant or animal is always written in *italics* (underlined if italic type is not available), and the genus name is always capitalized. The species name may be left uncapitalized, or, at the discretion of the writer, it may be capitalized if derived from the name of a person, deity, or genus.

The following list shows the classifications under which plants are grouped. Many taxonomists also make use of subdivisions, subclasses, subspecies (varieties), etc., to classify members of these groups more specifically.

Kingdom (Plantae)
Subkingdom
Division (or phylum)
Class
Order
Family
Genus (pl. genera)
Species

The supra classes Tracheophyta (the vascular plants) and Bryophyta (mosses and liverworts) may be thought of as constituting the subdivision Embryophytina. The subdivision Chlorophycophytina (green algae) and the other eight divisions (constituting the bacteria, various kinds of algae, and the fungi) form the subkingdom Thallophyta. Classification systems are presently in a state of flux, reflecting rapid advances in our understanding of the characteristics used to distinguish the various groups. For example, the single supra class that we call Tracheophyta is divided by other authors into four or five divisions, called here subdivisions.

The vascular plants are characterized by well-developed vascular or conducting tissue, through which solutions move from one part of the plant to another (see Chapters 7, 9, 11, and 12). The vegetative plant body is, in its simplest form, an axis made up of root and stem and bearing lateral appendages such as leaves and lateral roots. Plants have an *alternation of generations* during their life cycle (see Doyle, *Nonvascular Plants: Form and Function* in this series). The *gametophyte* produces *gametes,* which unite to form a *zygote,* the first cell of the *sporophyte* generation. This generation produces *spores* capable of growing into the gametophyte. In many of the nonvascular plants, the gametophyte is the dominant generation, and the sporophyte may be only one cell (the zygote) or a multicellular organism dependent or parasitic for its nutrition upon the gametophyte. Moving up the scale of classification, the sporophyte becomes more and more important, and in the vascular plants it becomes the dominant, conspicuous generation. The gametophyte is small, and in the conifers (*gymnosperms*) and flowering plants (*angiosperms*) it is parasitic upon the sporophyte (see Chapter 13).

A large number of the nearly 100,000 nonvascular plants are aquatic. (The fungi and the mosses make up more than half of this number, and although they usually require an abundance of water for active growth, they are not generally aquatic). Aquatic vascular plants are, on the other hand, the exception rather than the rule. There are about three times as many vascular-plant species as nonvascular-plant species. The classification system shown in Table 1-1 is used in this volume.

Table 1-1

Taxon	English Name	Approximate Number of Species
Division:		
Schizophyta	Bacteria	
Eumycota	Fungi	
Myxomycota	Slime molds	
Cyanophyta	Blue-green algae	
Rhodophyta	Red algae	
Chrysophyta	Golden algae and diatoms	95,000
Phaeophyta	Brown algae	
Euglenophyta	Euglenoids	
Chlorophyta	Green plants	
Subdivision:		
Chlorophycophytina	Green algae	5,700
Embryophytina	Embryo-forming plants	
Supra Class:		
Bryophyta	Mosses and liverworts	23,300
Tracheophyta	Vascular plants	
Class:		
Psilopsida	Psilophytes	30
Lycopsida	Club mosses or lycopods	1,200
Sphenopsida	Horsetails	40
Pteropsida	Ferns and seed-bearing plants	
Subclass:		
Filicidae	Ferns	9,000
Gymnospermidae	Conifers, cycads, and relatives	750
Angiospermidae	Flowering plants	
Series:		
Dicotyledoneae	Dicotyledonous plants	236,500
Monocotyledoneae	Monocotyledonous plants	48,500

Psilopsida

Living members of this class are restricted to two somewhat uncommon tropical genera, but many fossils from this group are known, and it has been suggested that all of the other vascular plants developed from this group. The plant body is extremely simple, lacking true roots or leaves, although root-like *rhizoids* are present on some of the fossils, as are leaf-like scales. The tubular plant body is dichotomously branched (main axis branches into two branches, which may in turn branch into two more, etc.), and vascular tissue is clearly evident, although simple in its organization. Spores are produced in *sporangia* (a unicellular or, as in this case, a multicellular receptacle) on the branches, and the gametophyte that develops from these spores is underground and associated with a fungus. The gametophyte is also tubular in form, resembling the sporophyte, and the sex organs are scattered over its surface. The *swimming sperm* (male gametes) have many *cilia* (hair-like organelles of locomotion). It is interesting to note that, primitive as these plants may be, there is a large gap between them and the most advanced nonvascular plants. At present, no living or fossil plants that might bridge this gap are known.

Lycopsida

Two living families—Lycopodiaceae and Selaginellaceae—represent this class, but again many fossil examples of this group have been found, some of which were of tree size. *Lycopodium* is considered to be a representative genus of the first family. In some species of this genus, the gametophyte is colorless and grows underground; in others it is green and above ground. In both cases it is always associated with a fungus. The main stem of the mature sporophyte is prostrate and freely branching, giving rise to upright stems several inches to a foot or more in height. Both kinds of stems are sheathed with small, simple green leaves. True adventitious roots occur on the prostrate stems. In *Lycopodium,* the pattern of organization of the vascular system of the stems resembles that of the roots of the flowering plants, rather than the stems. Spores are produced in sporangia on special leaves called *sporophylls,* which may be somewhat modified from vegetative leaves (in some species they are not so modified) and grouped together at the ends of the stem to form a *cone* or *strobilus.*

Selaginella is considered to be a representative genus of the second family. Most of the more than 500 species in this genus are tropical, but some occur in temperate zones. Some are very drought-resistant (such as the resurrection plant). The mature sporophyte resembles that of *Lycopodium,* except that the stems appear to be square, owing to the way in which the leaves are attached. Usually the upright branches are only a few inches high, but climbers reaching 50 feet in height are known in the tropics. The vascular system is somewhat advanced over that of *Lycopodium,* but is still relatively primitive. The sporophylls resemble foliage leaves but are grouped together at the end of branches to form stroboli, which may look like vegetative branches.

The formation of spores and gametophytes is advanced in certain respects over the examples above. First, two kinds of spores may be formed: *microspores* and *megaspores*. Second, the microspores may develop into a mature male gametophyte without leaving the sporophyll. Such microgametophytes produce *antheridia*, which in turn produce sperm. The megaspores, often germinating on sporophylls in the same strobilus as the microsporophylls, develop by a series of cell divisions into the female gametophyte, which remains within the megaspore almost until maturity is reached. *Archegonia* containing the eggs may receive the sperm while the female gametophyte is still on the sporophyll, or the female gametophyte may be shed before fertilization. If fertilization occurs before shedding, the process becomes quite similar to that in the seed plants. Third, the zygote develops into an *embryo* inside the female gametophyte (on or off of the sporophyll). The embryo is not capable of going into an extended period of dormancy, but if it were, the resemblance to the seed would be striking indeed.

Sphenopsida

This class is represented by only one living family with one living genus, *Equisetum*, although, like the two classes just discussed, many fossils belonging to this group are known. Although there are few species of the horsetails (a direct translation of the Latin *Equisetum*), they are widely distributed, occurring in most parts of the earth except Australia. Most species grow in moist places, but the common North American representative, *Equisetum arvense*, grows in dry habitats. The gametophyte is a small, green *thallus* (plant body without true roots, stems, or leaves) growing in the soil, and the zygote develops directly into an embryo and then a sporophyte. The sporophyte is characterized by green, ridged stems capable of photosynthesis, with reduced, scale-like leaves arising in whorls at the true nodes. (Meristematic tissue occurs at the nodes, and this is soft and easily separated, allowing the stem to be easily broken into segments.) The epidermal cells contain a considerable amount of deposited silica, and this gives them a roughness that once made them the efficient "scouring rushes" used by the pioneers. The organization of the vascular elements of the stems is relatively advanced. Spores are produced in strobili composed of special structures called *sporangiophores* (no resemblance to leaves is evident), consisting of shield-shaped disks supported by short stalks growing at right angles to the stem. Only one kind of spore is produced (no mega- or microspores), and attached to it are two filaments that straighten and coil in response to slight changes in atmospheric humidity. Figure 1-1 illustrates members of this and the other two subdivisions discussed so far.

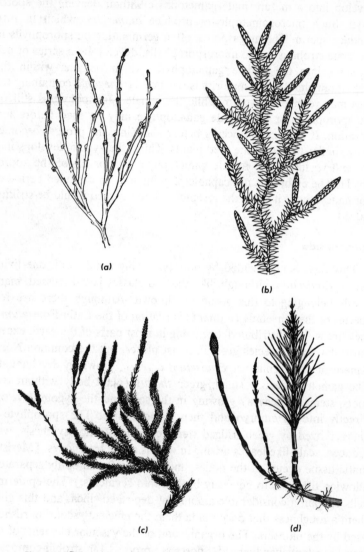

Fig. 1-1. *Some representatives of the lower vascular plants.* (*a*) Psilotum. *Dichotomous-branching and scale-like forked leaves.* (*b*) Selaginella. *Vegetative leaves and cones.* (*c*) Lycopodium. *Part of a prostrate stem with leafy, erect shoots bearing cones.* (*d*) Equisetum arvense. *A sterile shoot (right) and a fertile one (left), both growing from an underground rootstalk. Figs.* (*a*), (*c*), *and* (*d*) *from E. W. Sinnott and K. S. Wilson,* Botany: Principles and Problems *(McGraw-Hill Book Co., Inc., 1955), by permission;* (*b*) *from H. L. Dean,* Laboratory Exercises, Biology of Plants *(Wm. C. Brown Co., 1949), by permission.*

Pteropsida

According to one viewpoint, the three subclasses of Pteropsida might each have supra class or class status comparable to the three classes just discussed. Yet these three subclasses do have a number of things in common with each other that they do not share with the other three classes. Leaves are typically large enough to be readily seen (though much reduced in a few species), and the sporangia are more numerous and borne on true leaves, although in some cases they are modified. The vascular system is more advanced in certain respects (particularly in having leaf gaps—see Chapter 7). Some evolutionists believe that these three subclasses are all related to each other by evolutionary descent; in contrast, the three classes discussed previously may have evolved independently.

Whereas each of the previous three classes was well represented at one time or another in the earth's history but has since been reduced to minor importance, the Pteropsida make up the dominant and common vegetation of the earth today. Most of the remaining chapters of this volume are concerned with the characteristics of the Pteropsida, such as the detailed structure of the stems and roots and features of reproduction. The summary below emphasizes the characters that distinguish the subclasses. It should be noted that many points relating to internal stem anatomy and other characteristics, as discussed in the remaining chapters of this volume, have application (often with some modification) to the three classes just discussed as well as the Pteropsida.

Subclass I. Filicidae (ferns). Many fossil ferns are known, but the group is also represented by numerous living species. Ferns were not as common in ancient times as was formerly thought, since many of the fossils thought to be ferns proved to be seed plants (gymnosperms). Ferns typically grow in moist habitats, although certain fern species are known in dry regions. The sporophyte is dominant in the ferns, consisting usually of a rhizome (underground stem) bearing adventitious roots and upright leaves. The leaves are usually dissected into leaflets, arranged pinnately (feather-like) on a stout midrib. They grow by meristematic tissue at the tips, and are rolled into tight spirals that unwind as the leaves grow. The vascular system of ferns is well developed, although it is thought to be more primitive than that of the other subclasses of Pteropsida. The spores develop in sporangia, ordinarily on the undersurface of the leaves, sometimes near the margins. Not all leaves produce spores, and in some species the ones that do are different from the sterile ones. Sometimes the sporangia are grouped into *sori,* and in some of these cases the sorus is protected by an umbrella-like structure known as an *indusium*. The spores germinate and grow into the gametophyte, a flat, heart-shaped thallus having rhizoids on the bottom. The sex organs also form on the lower side, and sperm from the antheridia must swim to the archegonia to carry out fertilization. The zygote grows into an embryo that continues to develop into the mature sporophyte, completing the life cycle. Figure 1-2 illustrates the life cycle of a representative fern.

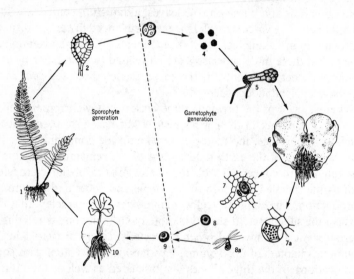

Fig. 1-2. *Life history of a fern. (1) Fern plant (sporophyte) bearing sori (clusters of sporangia) on its leaves. (2) Sporangium. (3) Tetrad of young spores. (4) Four mature spores that have come from the tetrad shown in (3). (5) Spore germinating into a young gametophyte. (6) Mature gametophyte bearing sexular organs. (7) Archegonium. (8) Antheridium. (9) Egg cell or female gamete. (10) Sperm or male gamete. (11) Young sporophyte growing out of a fertilized egg, the whole still attached to the remains of the gametophyte. From E. W. Sinnott and K. S. Wilson,* Botany: Principles and Problems *(McGraw-Hill Book Co., Inc., 1955), by permission.*

Subclass II. Gymnospermidae (conifers, cycads, Ginkgo, Gnetum, etc.). Members of this group all bear seeds, and the seeds occur on the surface of the sporophyll, not contained within an ovary, as are angiosperm seeds (see below). All forms in this group are trees or shrubs, but the variety of form is extensive. Some representatives are as rare and botanically interesting as those of the first three classes. There are the cycads, the forms of which are represented by many fossils; cycads are considered by some botanists to form a separate subclass. There is *Ginkgo biloba,* a single living genus and species in its family, and the only family in its order! Fossil "seed ferns" are considered to be gymnosperms. There are the three widely different genera placed in the order *Gnetales: Ephedra* (a shrub of desert regions in both hemispheres), *Gnetum* (a tropical shrub or climbing vine), and *Welwitschia* (a strange desert plant of western South Africa with two large, strap-shaped perennial leaves coming from a short, stout axis). Even within the order *Coniferales* there is a great deal of variety. There are the familiar pines, firs, spruces, hemlocks, Douglas firs, junipers, larches, yews, and redwoods. In addition there is *Araucaria* (the monkey puzzle tree) from the subtropics, and there are species in New Zealand and Australia that have broad leaves instead of the needle-like leaves or scales typical of those named above. Most but not all of the species have cones (for example, the junipers have fleshy scales and the yews have a pulpy, berry-like body at the base of the seeds).

The sporophyte is the dominant generation, and the gametophyte is completely parasitic upon it. The anatomy of the sporophyte and to a lesser extent the gametophyte will be referred to in the remaining chapters of this volume. Spores are produced in sporangia, which are located on the scales of the male (*staminate*) and female (*ovulate*) cones. The staminate cones bear microsporangia on the lower surfaces of the scales, and the ovulate cones bear megasporangia in ovules on the upper surfaces of the scales. The microspores are produced by meiosis and develop into the male gametophytes, which by further mitotic divisions develop into pollen grains. A few gymnosperms have motile, swimming sperm cells (notably *Ginkgo*), as do all members of the three previously discussed classes. The female gametophyte develops from a megaspore into a multicellular body somewhat more complex than the male gametophyte, but remaining parasitic upon the scale of the female cone. The female gametophyte produces an egg cell, which, after fertilization, becomes a zygote and then develops into an embryo capable of an extended period of dormancy. The embryo thus formed is part of a seed that is naked (not surrounded by the wall of an ovary). Figure 1-3 illustrates some important structures of a typical gymnosperm.

Subclass III. Angiospermidae (flowering plants): monocotyledoneae (monocots) and dicotyledoneae (dicots). The angiosperms are at present the dominant plants of this planet. Except for the waters of the world and the coniferous forests, the conspicuous vegetation is made up of the flowering plants. Most seem adapted in every way to the land habitat. They show a great variety of form: minute duckweeds, herbaceous forms such as grasses and forbs, succulents such as the cacti, various shrubs, and trees of all shapes and sizes including the

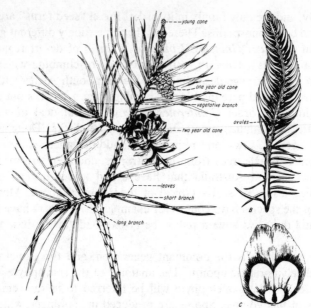

Fig. 1-3. *Some features of a familiar conifer. (A) Branch of pine with leaves and ovulate cones. (B) Ovulate cone of spruce cut longitudinally to show scales with ovules. (C) Detail of one scale with two ovules. Drawings by Elsie M. McDougle, from J. B. Hill et al.,* Botany *(McGraw-Hill Book Co., Inc., 1960), by permission.*

large eucalyptus of Australia. In spite of this variety in form, it is possible to recognize certain features of the angiosperm plant body (the sporophyte) such as the roots (fibrous or taproot system, with no true appendages similar to leaves), and the shoots with stems having *nodes* and *internodes* and appendages arising at the nodes. The leaves, consisting of *blades* and *petioles,* are the most common appendages, but lateral branches form from buds in the leaf *axils* just above the base of the leaf. Flowers and fruits may form at the axils or at the stem apex. Figure 1-4 shows the generalized angiosperm plant body.

The outstanding and unique structures of the Angiospermidae are the flower and the fruit that subsequently develops from the ovary of the flower. The seeds develop enclosed within this ovary. These structures are discussed in detail in Chapters 13 and 17.

The gametophyte has been reduced to the pollen grain and developing pollen tube (male) and the embryo sac within an ovule (female) —structures discussed in Chapter 13. These gametophyte structures are completely parasitic upon the sporophyte.

The vascular system shows its most advanced characteristics in members of the Angiospermidae (see Chapters 7 and 9).

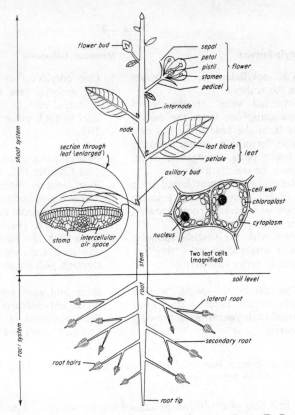

Fig. 1-4. *The parts of a seed plant (diagrammatic). From F. D. Kern, "The Essentials of Plant Biology" (Harper & Row, Publishers, 1947), by permission.*

The angiosperms are readily divided into two series: the Dicotyledonae and the Monocotyledoneae. Table 1-2 summarizes some of the features that characterize the two groups. Although the Dicotyledoneae and the Monocotyledoneae are clearly distinct from each other, no single character listed in Table 1-2 occurs in only one group. The characters are, however, reliable in the great majority of cases. We will refer to these two groups frequently in later chapters.

Taxonomists are not agreed on the evolutionary relationships among the angiosperms, but many American botanists still utilize the classification system of Charles E. Bessey, a professor at the University of Nebraska from the last part of the nineteenth century to 1915. Bessey suggested that the order of flowering plants retaining the greatest number of primitive characters was the Ranales, including the magnolia and the buttercups. It was suggested that evolution from the ancient ancestors of the Ranales progressed in three directions.

Table 1-2*

Dicotyledoneae	Monocotyledoneae
1. Two cotyledons or seed leaves in the embryo.	1. One cotyledon or seed leaf in the embryo (see Chapter 17).
2. Principal veins of the leaves branching out from the midrib or from the base of it, not parallel, forming a distinct network.	2. Principal veins of the leaves parallel to each other (see Chapter 10).
3. Flower parts arranged in twos, fours, or usually fives.	3. Flower parts arranged in threes (see Chapter 13).
4. Root system characterized by a taproot—that is, a large primary root with branch roots growing from it.	4. Root system fibrous—that is, without a principal or taproot, the evident roots being of about the same size (see Chapter 7).
5. Stem with the vascular bundles in a single cylinder ("ring" as seen in cross section).	5. Stem with the vascular bundles scattered apparently irregularly through pith tissue (see Chapter 7).
6. The cambium adding a new cylindroidal layer ("ring") of wood each year or each growing season.	6. Stem and root without a cambium, not increasing in girth by the formations of annual cylindroidal layers of wood (see Chapter 9).

* From Lyman Benson, *Plant Classification* (Boston: D.C. Heath & Co., 1957). Used by permission.

The first line of evolution produced the monocots. In addition to certain relatively small groups, the monocots are presently represented by three groups of plants well known to most people: the grasses (including wheat, the cereals, and maize—plants of considerable economic importance), the lilies, and the palms.

The second line of evolution gave rise to plants having *inferior* ovaries (see Chapter 13). A center of evolution in this line was the Rosales (some of which have inferior or partially inferior ovaries), including the strawberry, the rose, the apple and related fruits, and the legumes (for example, the pea, bean, and clover). From the ancestors of the Rosales, a number of other families, with separated petals, seem to have developed, such as the cactus, the myrtle (including the eucalyptus), the carrot, and the dogwood. Flowers in this line with united petals are the squashes, the honeysuckles, and the large family of composites (the sunflower, daisy, dandelion, thistle, cocklebur, aster, ragweed, sagebrush, goldenrod, and their many relatives).

Bessey suggested that the third line of evolution centered around the geraniums, but other groups may have been as important as this

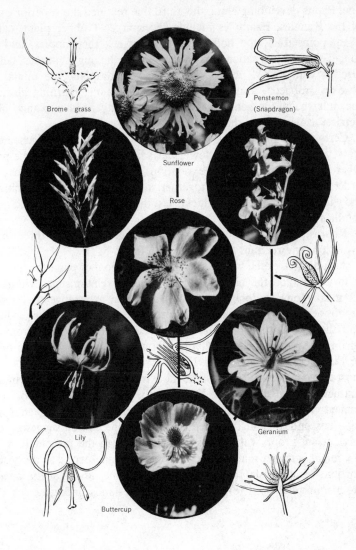

Fig. 1-5. *Some representatives of the angiosperms or flowering plants, arranged according to the evolutionary scheme proposed by Bessey. The* Ranales *(buttercup—Ranunculus adoneus* Gray*) are considered most primitive, with evolution proceeding in three directions: (1) through the Liliales (lily—Erythronium grandiflorum* Pursh*) to the grasses (Bromus inermis* Leyss.*); (2) through the Rosales (Rosa acicularis* Lindl.*) to the composites ("sunflower," Old-Man-of-the-Mountain,* Hymenoxys grandiflora *[*Pursh*] Parker); and (3) through the Geraniales (Geranium fremontii* Torr.*) to examples such as the snapdragons and penstemons (*Penstemon secundiflorus *Benth.). The schematic diagrams indicate changes in position of the ovaries (stippled) and in shape of the corolla (petals).*

one. Plants developing along this third line retained the superior ovary of the Ranales. Examples include the spurges (rubber plant, castor bean, poinsettia), the hollyhocks, the violets, the poppies, and the four-o'clocks (carnation, buckwheat), all having separate petals. Groups with united petals include the snapdragons, the mints, the phloxes (tobacco, tomato, potato, forget-me-nots, morning glories), the milkweeds, the gentians, the heaths (many heather plants, blueberries, azaleas), and the primroses.

Certain of the flowering plants did not fit well into the scheme of Bessey, often because their flower parts had been reduced to the point where it was difficult to see relationships with other families and orders. These were lumped together into the Amentiferae, including the willows, the walnuts, the hickories, the oaks, the birches, and other families or genera.

Representative species from the Ranales and the three main evolutionary directions are illustrated in Fig. 1-5.

As indicated at the first of this chapter, the goal of plant taxonomists is to understand the natural or evolutionary relationships within the plant kingdom. In doing so, it is a temptation to arrange the existing groups according to the number of primitive features that they exhibit, and then to assume that the "advanced" groups evolved from the "primitive" ones. Yet no individual in a living group of plants could be the ancestor of any other living taxonomic group of plants. The most that can be said is that some modern groups retain more primitive characters than others. The Ranales, then, are descendants of some ancient group, and the lilies or the sunflowers or the snapdragons may have descended from the same ancient group. Bessey suggested that this ancient group was similar in many ways to the present Ranales. We might imagine that the modern taxa are analogous to the visible portions of coral islands in a rising sea of time, and that the ancient groups are analogous to the bases of these islands under the sea.

2

THE GENERALIZED
PLANT CELL

Certain species of lower plants and animals (algae, fungi, protozoans) are single-celled organisms throughout their entire life span. In the developmental cycles of sexually reproducing higher plants and animals, the diploid organism is initiated as a single cell, the *zygote*. The time interval that such an organism remains as a single cell is usually very brief, however, and through continuous and rapid cell division a multicellular embryo is produced, which then gives rise to a complex, mature organism made up of many different types of cells, tissues, and organs.

This cellular organization of the plant body was first recognized by Robert Hooke in 1665. He applied the term "cell" to the individual units of structure composing the cork tissue he had observed under a primitive microscope. In 1839 two German scientists, M. J. Schleiden, a botanist, and Theodor Schwann, a zoologist, formulated the *cell theory,* which states that *in most living organisms the cell is the fundamental unit of structure and function*. It is interesting to note that, while Schleiden and Schwann succeeded in focusing attention on the theory and are usually given credit for its formulation, at least six other investigators had previously expressed similar views! In 1880 J. Hanstein used the term "protoplast" to designate the entire contents of the cell exclusive of the cell wall. This term should not be confused with *protoplasm,* the generalized living matter of the cell.

A convenient means of outlining the composition of a generalized green plant cell is as follows (see Fig. 2-1):

A. Cell wall (may contain numerous strands of cytoplasm)
B. Protoplast
    1. Protoplasmic ("living") parts
        (a) Cytoplasm
        (b) Nucleus
        (c) Plastids
        (d) Mitochondria

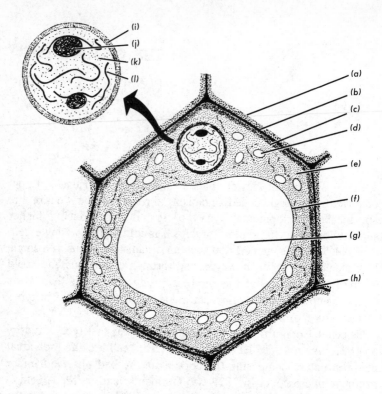

Fig. 2-1. *Diagram of a generalized plant cell and enlarged view of the nucleus. The endoplasmic reticulum and golgeosome are not included. (a) Primary wall. (b) Middle lamella. (c) Plasmalemma. (d) Chloroplast. (e) Mitochondrium. (f) Tonoplast. (g) Vacuole. (h) Intercellular space. (i) Nuclear membrane. (j) Nucleolus. (k) Nuclear sap. (l) Chromonema.*

2. Nonprotoplasmic ("nonliving") parts
   (a) Vacuoles
   (b) Ergastic substances
      (1) Starch grains
      (2) Crystals, etc.

THE CELL WALL

One of the most conspicuous differences between plant and animal cells is the presence, in the plant cell, of a relatively fully permeable wall surrounding and enclosing the protoplast. The wall is usually defined as nonliving, although in the young, rapidly expanding cell

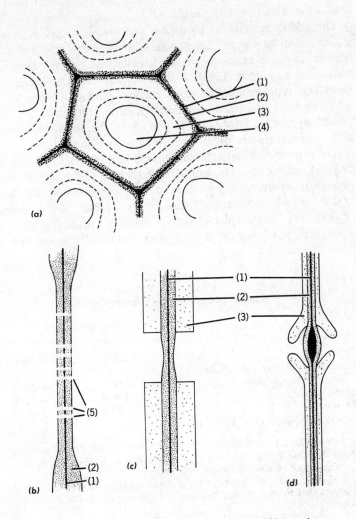

Fig. 2-2. *Diagrams illustrating (a) cell wall layers, (b) a primary pit field, (c) cross section of a simple pit, and (d) cross section of a bordered pit. (1) Middle lamella. (2) Primary wall. (3) Secondary wall. (4) Cell lumen. (5) Plasmodesmata.*

such a concept could be challenged. Plant cell walls are usually composed of two and sometimes three distinct layers (Fig. 2-2): (1) the *middle lamella,* which is formed during telophase of mitosis (cell division) and acts as a cementing substance between adjacent cells; (2) the *primary wall,* formed while the cell is still actively enlarging or elongating; and (3) in some cases, the *secondary wall,* formed inside the primary wall at a time when the cell is nearing or has reached maximum enlargement.

The middle lamella is amorphous and colloidal, and is composed mainly of various pectic substances such as pectic acid and calcium pectate. In some cases the middle lamella may become impregnated with lignin or suberin. Lignin is an amorphous, high molecular weight substance representing the condensation product of one or more aromatic hydrocarbons. Suberin and cutin are fatty substances made up of polymerized fatty acids. Lignin allows the passage of water, but cutin and suberin are highly impermeable to water.

The primary wall is the first finite wall layer formed by a developing cell and may be the only wall layer (exclusive of the middle lamella) present in many types of cells (such as parenchyma, collenchyma, and sieve-tube elements). Chemically the primary wall is composed of cellulose, noncellulosic polysaccharides, hemicelluloses, pectic substances, and protein. Lignin, cutin, and suberin are sometimes

Table 2-1

Chemical Composition of Primary Cell Walls*

CELL WALL CONSTITUENT	PERCENTAGES	
	ONE ANALYSIS†	RANGE OF VALUES‡
Cellulose	42%	20–50%
Noncellulosic polysaccharides and hemicelluloses	38%	4–51%
Pectic substances	8%	1–53%
Proteins	12%	3–30%
Lipids (e.g., cutin and suberin)	–	1–24%

* From G. Setterfield and S. T. Bayley, "Structure and Physiology of Cell Walls." *Annual Review of Plant Physiology,* Vol. 12 (1961), pp. 35–62.

† One set of results for the oat coleoptile.

‡ Maximum and minimum values from 21 analyses. (Zero values in some analyses [not shown] usually indicate that the substance was not measured.)

found as constituents of primary walls. Table 2-1 summarizes the constituents of plant cell walls. The primary wall is capable of extensive growth in surface, varies in thickness according to the metabolic state of the cell, and is generally associated with living protoplasts.

Cells that are involved in water conduction and in strengthening activities usually have secondary walls. Such layers are often quite thick, are nonreversible in the sense that once formed they are apparently not thinned down or removed, and in many cases consist in part of lignin or suberin.

THE PROTOPLASMIC PARTS OF THE CELL

The cytoplasm, itself highly organized, forms the living ground substance of the cell. In it are dispersed various specialized protoplasmic bodies or organelles. In the living, untreated cell, the cytoplasm, when viewed with a light microscope, appears as a translucent, structureless, homogeneous substance containing refractile bodies of varying sizes. It is bounded externally by the *plasma membrane* or *plasmalemma* and internally by the *tonoplast* or *vacuolar membrane*. Both the plasma membrane and the tonoplast are differentially permeable membranes and hence are of great importance in such cellular activities as osmosis. Cytoplasm is a complex colloidal substance with a chemical makeup approximately as follows: water, 85 to 90 per cent; proteins, 7 to 10 per cent; carbohydrates, 1 per cent; lipids, 1 per cent; and various inorganic compounds, such as calcium, in small amounts. Recent evidence from electron microscopy provides ample proof that the cytoplasm is highly organized into a system of cavities or vesicles surrounded by a complex interwoven network of membranes (endoplasmic reticulum) and is not, in actuality, a "structureless, homogeneous" material as it was once thought to be.

The *nucleus* is conspicuous as a large, spherical body surrounded by cytoplasm and bounded externally by a double-layered structure termed the *nuclear membrane* (Fig. 2-1). The differentially permeable nature of the nuclear membrane is presently being challenged. Electron micrographs show the presence of pores or discontinuities in this envelope and also indicate continuity between the outer part of the nuclear membrane and the endoplasmic reticulum. Within the nuclear membrane occur the *chromonemata,* embedded in a clear, sometimes viscous fluid, the *nuclear sap*. The chromonemata are extremely important in that they become the *chromosomes* during meiotic and mitotic divisions and are the carriers of the *genes*—molecular aggregations of deoxyribonucleic acid (DNA). One view of chromonema structure holds that these hereditary units consist of chains of protein molecules forming the "backbone" of the structure, to which are attached in linear sequence the various DNA macromolecules. Interphasic nuclei usually contain large, spherical, deep-staining bodies that are formed in association with specific regions of certain chromonemata. These structures are termed *nucleoli* and are apparently directly involved in the synthesis of nuclear ribonucleic acid (RNA) and proteins.

Plant cells usually contain specialized cytoplasmic bodies called *plastids*. These structures are separated into three main types on the basis of color. Green plastids are called *chloroplasts,* orange and yellow plastids are called *chromoplasts,* and colorless plastids are called *leucoplasts.* Chloroplasts are extremely important cellular components, because those found in vascular plants contain the two green pigments, chlorophyll A and chlorophyll B, and two orange-yellow pigments, carotene and xanthophyll, and these four pigments must be present if photosynthesis (the process whereby sunlight is converted into chemical energy) is to occur. Leucoplasts are often involved in food-storage activities, such as starch formation and oil synthesis.

All living cells, both plant and animal, contain small rod-like or spherical structures termed *mitochondria.* These bodies play an important part in cell respiration and have been referred to as the "powerhouses" of the cell.

In addition to nuclei, plastids, and mitochondria, other protoplasmic structures, such as the *Golgi* complex and the *centriole,* may be encountered in plant cells. The Golgi complex is a membrane system similar to the endoplasmic reticulum in many instances but lacking ribonucleoprotein granules (and hence designated a "smooth" membrane system). The centriole or cell center is probably directly involved in the synthesis of fibrillar proteins.

THE NONPROTOPLASMIC PARTS OF THE CELL

At maturity the generalized plant cell contains a single, large, centrally located cavity, the *vacuole,* which is separated from the cytoplasm by the vacuolar membrane and which consists of a complex water solution, the *cell sap.* In the young embryonic cell, vacuoles exist in the form of many small, dispersed units. With enlargement and maturation of the cell, the vacuoles increase greatly in volume, coalesce, and eventually form one large structure that may occupy 95 per cent of the total cell volume. Present in the vacuole are a large number of organic and inorganic substances. Water is the main vacuolar component. Other vacuolar constituents that may be encountered are red, blue, and purple anthocyanin pigments, organic acids, fats, tannins, and crystals of various types. Such vacuolar constituents as those just listed most often represent metabolic by-products and reserve food materials. Starch grains, amino acids, oils, various types of proteins, and dissolved salts are also common vacuolar materials.

CELLS AND TISSUES

Thus the plant cell must be thought of as a complex and highly organized unit made up of fully integrated living and nonliving systems performing a wide variety of physiologic activities. During the evolution of the vegetative organs of higher plants, much cellular specialization has occurred, resulting in the development and perpetuation of diverse cell types. (Cells of a given type, or those performing a single important physiological activity, are often aggregated together, forming a tissue. Tissues are united, forming tissue systems, and the various tissue systems form an organ. All of the organs, collectively, constitute the organism.) The least specialized cell type found in the bodies of higher plants is generally considered to be the *parenchyma* cell. These cells usually have thin primary walls, function as living cells, and are able to perform a wide variety of physiological activities. In contrast, the wood fiber is a highly specialized cell type. These cells have thick lignified secondary walls at maturity, lose their protoplasts when mature, and perform a single function—that of mechanical support—as dead elements. Other cell types composing the plant body will be listed and described in succeeding chapters.

3

SOME BASIC
PLANT FUNCTIONS

Cellular processes were discussed in the first volume of this series (Jensen: *The Plant Cell*), so they will be only briefly summarized here, except for the processes of diffusion and osmosis. They are developed here because of their direct application to our discussion of translocation and the ascent of sap (Chapter 12).

DIFFUSION

Probably some of the most fundamental information derived from the sciences of physics and chemistry is the knowledge that many natural events may be interpreted in light of the *kinetic activity* of molecules and particles of molecular size. Temperature results from the average momentum or kinetic energy of such particles. The velocities of particles of a given size (such as molecules in a gas) are not constant but are varied and distributed according to the curves shown in Fig. 3-1. The *average* velocity of all such particles depends upon the temperature. Since it is the average momentum (mass times velocity) that is constant for a given temperature, small particles will have a higher average velocity than large ones having the same momentum.

This rather simple approach to an understanding of matter allows us to understand a great many things. We know, for example, that a liquid becomes a gas (boils) when the kinetic energies of its molecules are so great that the forces of attraction between them are insufficient to hold them together in the liquid state. Below the boiling point, only those molecules evaporate that, because of the random distribution of their energies, have sufficient energy to overcome the bonding forces. These same high-energy particles are important in the chemical reactions and other processes taking place in plants.

A phenomenon that is of considerable importance to plant function is that of *diffusion,* which is a net movement of molecular-sized

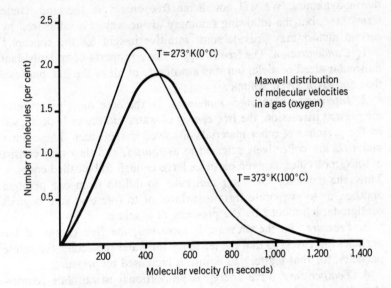

Fig. 3-1. *The number of molecules in gaseous oxygen as a function of their velocity. Note that the peak shifts to higher velocities at higher temperatures. The increase in molecules of highest velocity (the ones most likely to react chemically, evaporate if the substance were a liquid, etc.) is especially striking.*

particles from one point to another, and this is a function of their kinetic activity. In the simplest case, the movement occurs in response to differences in concentration. We can roughly visualize the mechanism by thinking of two rooms connected by a window—one room filled with white balls and the other with black balls. The balls have perfect elasticity and are in motion, colliding and bouncing off each other in the same way that molecular particles do. Obviously there is a certain probability that some of the black balls will go through the window instead of striking the walls. Of course, white ones will go in the opposite direction. As more and more black ones go through the window, the concentration (number per unit volume) decreases in the one chamber and increases in the other. Finally there will be approximately an equal number of black balls and white balls in both rooms, and the chances that they will go from left to right will be about the same as the chances that they will go from right to left. This is *equilibrium*.

Yet diffusion is not strictly a function of the concentration gradient. More accurately, it occurs in response to a gradient in *free energy* of the particles. The concept of free energy is one developed after considerable foundation-laying in courses in physical chemistry and thermodynamics. We will not define free energy in thermodynamic terms here, but the following summary of the way it is influenced by certain factors may provide some intuitive insight for the concept.*

1. *Concentration*. The free energy is not a property of an individual molecular-sized particle, but it is a property of all the like particles that occupy a given volume.

2. *Interaction with other molecules*. In the case most germane to the present discussion, the free energy of water molecules is decreased by the presence of other materials dissolved in the water. These other materials are collectively referred to as *solutes*, and they may consist of ions, molecules, or even particles large enough to be called *colloids*. Thus, the tendency for water molecules to diffuse from one point to another, or to evaporate from a surface, or to freeze at zero degrees centigrade, is reduced by the presence of a solute.

3. *Pressure*. As the pressure is increased, the free energy of the particles increases, so that the tendency for water molecules (or solute particles, for that matter) to diffuse is increased by pressure.

4. *Temperature*. Free energy is proportional to absolute temperature (centigrade temperature plus 273°). Thus, if the temperature in one part of the system differs from that in another part, the tendency to diffuse is influenced.

These are the factors that might be important in the establishment of a free-energy gradient leading to diffusion. The actual rate of diffusion, once such a gradient has been established, is influenced by the following factors.

1. *Steepness of the free-energy gradient*. The steepness of the free-energy gradient influences the rate. The steeper the gradient, the more rapidly diffusion will occur (from areas of high free energy to areas of low free energy).

2. *Velocity*. The velocity of the molecular-sized particles influences diffusion rate. Thus, the smaller the particles the greater their average velocity at a given temperature, and the greater their diffusion rate. For a given-sized particle, increasing temperature also increases velocity, but this is proportional to absolute temperature.

3. *Permeability of the medium*. Movement of the particles occurs through a medium of some sort, and the permeability of this medium will determine the rate of diffusion. Thus, the diffusion of solute particles in water depends on the permeability of the water to the solute, and diffusion of water through a membrane depends on the permeability of the membrane to water molecules.

---

* The term *diffusion pressure* has been used in essentially the same context.

If two species of molecular-sized particles do not interact with each other chemically in some way, one will not influence the diffusion of the other. Each will diffuse according to its own free-energy gradient at rates influenced by temperature and permeability.

OSMOSIS

The phenomenon of *osmosis* is a special case of diffusion. The essential feature of an osmotic system is the presence of a membrane that will maintain, for a reasonable time interval, concentration and pressure differences on either side. Thus, in the typical osmometer (Fig. 3-2) we might have a solution of sugar, or any other solute,

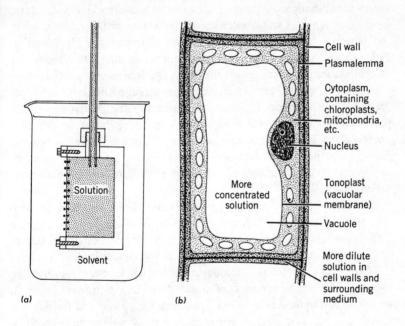

Fig. 3-2. (*a*) *Mechanical osmometer.* (*b*) *The cell as an osmotic system.*

separated by a membrane from water. It is usually stated that the membrane is *semipermeable,* implying that it will allow passage of water molecules but not solute particles. But it does so only to a first approximation, since water molecules are themselves somewhat retarded in passage through most membranes, and a great many solutes will eventually cross the membrane. Thus, most real membranes are only *differentially permeable,* but for the purposes of our discussion we may think in terms of a truly semipermeable membrane.

The presence of the solute particles within the membrane decreases the free energy of the water molecules. This establishes a free-energy gradient, with high free energies (of water) on the outside of the membrane and low free energies on the inside of the membrane. Water, then, will tend to diffuse into the osmometer. Of course, there is an infinitely steep free-energy gradient for the solute, from inside to outside, but since the solute particles cannot pass through the membrane, this gradient cannot be relieved by diffusion.

As water molecules move into the system, there is a dilution of the solution inside. In many cases this dilution is not important and can be ignored. A much more important effect is a buildup of pressure, which may occur due to the rigidity of the cell wall, if the osmometer under consideration is a plant cell, or by establishment of a hydrostatic head (a column of water exerting pressure due to its weight), as in the typical laboratory osmometer. Both instances are illustrated in Fig. 3-2. As pressure increases, free energy of the water molecules also increases. At some given pressure, the free energy of the water molecules within the osmometer becomes equal to the free energy of the water molecules on the outside of the osmometer. When this occurs there will no longer be a gradient in free energy, and so diffusion (osmosis) will stop. Of course water molecules will still be moving through the membrane because of their kinetic activity, but rate of movement in one direction will equal rate of movement in the other direction.

This explanation of osmosis probably comes as close to a description of the true state of affairs as anything available, yet a complete understanding of osmosis must depend upon knowledge of the nature of the membrane, and such knowledge is incomplete today.

Many incorrect interpretations of osmosis have been proposed in the past. The most common of these states that diffusion occurs in response to differences in water concentration inside and outside the membrane. It is stated that the presence of solute decreases the concentration of the water. In many cases this is simply not true. The concentration of water (number of water molecules per unit volume) does not change in instances where the addition of solute does not change the volume of the resulting solution. In some cases, concentration of water is slightly influenced by the addition of solute, but in no case can this influence be used to explain the quantitative aspects of osmosis. Osmosis depends upon the number of solute particles compared to the number of water molecules, and it is essentially independent of possible volume changes in the water brought about by the addition of solute.

THE OSMOTIC QUANTITIES

Physiologists have long felt the need to apply quantitative terms to the phenomenon of osmosis. Although the concept of free energy provides the best understanding of the process, free-energy values cannot be calculated except in a relative sense. The physiologist does not encounter abstract energy relationships in his measurements anyway; rather he deals with the pressures of turgid tissues, and a system based on these pressures had been developed before the concept of free energy was clarified. Three basic terms were established, and they are still in very wide use. Unfortunately their application is, in a sense, opposite to the discussion of free energy given above. The first of these terms is that of *osmotic potential,* referred to in many books as osmotic pressure or osmotic concentration. This is a property of a solution stated in pressure terms. Thus, if a given solution is placed in a perfect osmometer (perfectly semipermeable membrane, rigid walls allowing no change in volume), which is in turn placed in pure water, and a pressure of 10 atmospheres develops, we say that the solution has an osmotic potential of 10 atmospheres. This is true for the solution, even when it is standing in an open beaker on the laboratory bench. Knowing the molal concentration ($m =$ moles per 1000 grams of water), the temperature ($T =$ degrees absolute), a factor accounting for ionization (i), and the gas constant ($R = 0.082$ atm/molal degree), we can easily calculate the osmotic potential (ϕ): $\phi = miRT$. We can also calculate osmotic potential from the freezing point, boiling point, or vapor pressure of a solution. For example, the osmotic potential is equal to the depression of the freezing point (Δ) multiplied by a constant: $\phi = 12.04\Delta$.

The second term is *pressure* (P), which has been referred to as turgor pressure or wall pressure, and sometimes a distinction is made between these two. From the standpoint of free energy we are concerned only with pressure as such.

The third term is the final measure, at constant temperature, of the tendency for pure water at 1 atmosphere pressure to enter a given system by diffusion. The term *enter tendency* arises most naturally from the definition as stated, but it has most frequently been called *diffusion pressure deficit.** The enter tendency (E) of a part of an osmotic system is equal to its osmotic potential minus its pressure: $E = \phi - P$. Figure 3-3 illustrates graphically the relationship between these factors as cell volume increases by absorption of water.

---

* *Diffusion pressure deficit* is a logical term when the phenomenon is developed from the concept of diffusion pressure, but it seems unnecessarily cumbersome and will not be used here. The concept of *enter tendency* has had 18 to 20 different names since it was first put forth.

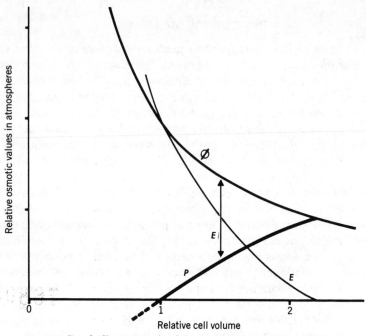

Fig. 3-3. *Graph illustrating the three osmotic quantities as they vary with changes in cell volume. Osmotic potential ($\emptyset$) is a function of concentration; thus, assuming no change in solute inside the cell, the $\emptyset$ curve is derived directly from volume (according to the formula $\emptyset = K/V$, where K is a constant). The pressure curve P, on the other hand, is an arbitrary one. It will depend on the mechanical properties of the cell wall and may vary from cell to cell. The enter tendency curve E is derived by subtracting the P curve from the $\emptyset$ curve, as shown.*

In our discussion of osmosis we have seen that the process occurs in response to a gradient in free energies—water moving from a point of high free energy to a point of low free energy. The presence of a solute decreases the free energy of the water and pressure increases it. The concept of enter tendency is analogous but opposite. Water molecules move from points of low enter tendency to points of high enter tendency, and the presence of a solute increases the enter tendency while pressure decreases it. Free energies should be stated in energy terms, but enter tendencies are stated in pressure terms, making the system of practical value to the physiologist. In either case, it is important to remember that no net diffusion occurs when there is no difference in either free energies or enter tendencies between the different parts of a system.

In advanced courses, these concepts are applied by working various problems. We will consider a single example. If cell A has an osmotic potential of 8 atmospheres (a rather typical value) and it is placed in pure water, a pressure of 8 atmospheres will develop. At that time the enter tendency will be equal to zero, the same as that of the surrounding pure water. If cell B has an osmotic potential of 6 atmospheres and it is placed in a solution having an osmotic potential of 2 atmospheres, pressure will develop within the cell to 4 atmospheres, at which time the enter tendency both inside and outside the cell will be equal at 2 atmospheres. If the two cells are now removed from their solutions and brought into contact with each other, water will move from cell A (where $E = 0$ atm) to cell B (where $E = 2$ atm).

While we are at it, let us allow cell A to double its volume as it takes up water. This will cut the concentration in half, so that the osmotic potential equals 4 atmospheres and the pressure that develops will also equal 4 atmospheres. Yet the enter tendency will still be equal to zero at equilibrium, because that is the enter tendency of the surrounding water. If the two cells are brought into contact, water will still move from A to B.

MOVEMENT OF SOLUTES THROUGH MEMBRANES

In Jensen: *The Plant Cell,* the movement of solutes through membranes was discussed. Three conclusions should be kept in mind while studying this volume:

1. Small, fat-soluble molecules penetrate the cell membrane best.

2. Ions interact with each other in their passage through membranes, producing the phenomenon known as *antagonism.* Thus, sodium ions in the absence of other cations may penetrate at rates so rapid that they become highly toxic to the cell. If trace amounts of calcium ions are added, however, this sodium toxicity is no longer apparent.

3. In the phenomenon of active *accumulation,* ions move *against* a free-energy gradient. In common instances, concentrations build up within the cell to levels more than a thousand times greater than those outside the cell, although in some instances concentrations outside are maintained exceedingly high compared to inside. This phenomenon requires the energy produced by metabolism.

RESPIRATION

Many of the plant's functions, such as ion accumulation, are dependent upon energy. In *The Plant Cell,* the processes of energy transfer in the living cell were discussed. Conclusions from a detailed discussion of respiration can be briefly summarized as follows:

1. A summary formula for the process is:

$$C_6H_{12}O_6 + 6O_2 \xrightarrow[\text{cell}]{\text{living}} 6CO_2 + 6H_2O + 674 \text{ Kcal.}$$

2. Although the formula shows glucose or fructose as the substrate, various other compounds, such as other carbohydrates, fats, or amino acids, may also be oxidized in the respiratory process.

3. Respiration of carbohydrate is known to involve about 40 enzymatically controlled steps.

4. The enzymatic steps divide into two main phases: (1) Carbohydrate may be degraded by *glycolysis* (oxidation of carbohydrates to pyruvic acid or related compounds) and/or a series of steps involving pentose phosphate. (2) The products of glycolysis may pass through the *Krebs Cycle,* in which two carbons are added to oxaloacetic acid to form citric acid, and this is gradually broken down to form oxaloacetic acid again. Krebs Cycle reactions occur on the mitochondria probably in conjunction with soluble enzymes of cytoplasm.

5. Many aspects of metabolism, such as fat and protein metabolism, are connected through certain enzymatic steps to the reactions of respiration. Certain of these reactions involve transfers of a two-carbon group to and from the compound coenzyme-A.

6. Compounds of phosphate are important, including phosphorylated intermediates, the energy-rich ATP, and pyridine nucleotides.

7. Much of the ATP is produced in a series of hydrogen or electron transfers through the enzyme system characterized by the *cytochromes*.

PHOTOSYNTHESIS

Some conclusions of photosynthesis studies (also discussed in Volume I) follow:

1. Light energy is converted into the chemical bond energy of carbohydrates and other compounds (such as amino acids). The following formula summarizes the process as it relates to carbohydrates:

$$2nH_2O^* + nCO_2 + \text{light energy} \xrightarrow[\text{plasts}]{\text{chloro-}} (CH_2O)_n + nO_2^* + nH_2O$$

2. Packets of light energy (quanta or photons) are absorbed by chlorophyll. A result in higher plants is the splitting of water with the production of free oxygen (see asterisks in formula above) and reduced (hydrogenated) pyridine nucleotides (PNH) and ATP. The processes are enzymatically controlled (that is, they require the presence of organic catalysts or enzymes).

3. Carbon dioxide is combined with a phosphorylated five-carbon compound in reactions independent of light. The resulting six-carbon compound splits, and using the energy of ATP and PNH and the hydrogen of PNH, carbohydrates are built up in a series of enzymatic reactions. The five-carbon compound is also produced to complete the cycle.

GENES, RIBOSOMES, AND ENZYMES

Some of the most spectacular discoveries during the 1950s were concerned with the manner in which enzymes are synthesized in the cell. This is discussed in Jensen: *The Plant Cell* and in Cook: *Reproduction, Heredity, and Sexuality.* We have learned, for example, that the genetic material controlling the inherited features of a plant—virtually everything about the plant—consists of macromolecules of deoxyribonucleic acid (DNA). Working out the structure of the macromolecule has shown us how it might reproduce. The two chains that form the double helix of the molecule are bonded to each other by complementary bonding, so that if one is separated from the other, its partner can be synthesized when the single chain is used as a template. The arrangement of nucleotide links in the chains seems to constitute the source of genetic information, which ultimately controls the synthesis of specific enzymes. This information from a single gene is transferred to the ribonucleic acid (RNA) of a ribosome and is subsequently used to order the arrangement of amino acids in a protein, resulting in a specific enzyme.

These three fundamental plant functions—respiration, photosynthesis, and gene metabolism—are basic to the topics discussed in this book. The structures outlined in the chapters on morphology owe their specific nature to these processes. That is, we think of the synthesis of specific structures in response to the activity of enzymes, and the fundamental process itself is dependent upon gene and enzyme metabolism and the energy transfers of photosynthesis and respiration.

4

GROWTH

The process of growth probably epitomizes plant and animal function more than any other activity of the living organism. All of the cellular structures and functions summarized briefly in Chapters 2 and 3 and discussed in detail in Jensen: *The Plant Cell* are an intrinsic part of the process of growth. Furthermore, of the many questions remaining in biology, some of the most intriguing and exciting ones are concerned with growth. We shall introduce some of the problems in this chapter, and much of the remainder of the book will be devoted to a further description of these problems and some of the current areas of research devoted to their solution. We have very few answers that even approach being final; however, the frontiers have been established.

ANALYSIS OF THE CONCEPT OF GROWTH

The term *growth* proves to have more connotations than one might at first imagine. The usual dictionary sense of the word implies the "progressive development of an organism," but the biologist recognizes two aspects of growth in the broad sense. He usually restricts the term *growth* to the first aspect, an increase in size or volume.* Growth in this sense has many close analogies in the inorganic world, such as the growth of a crystal by the addition of standard units to itself in a regular, orderly fashion.

The second aspect of growth is an increase in complexity, called *differentiation*. Both growth in the restricted sense and differentiation are essential to growth in the broad sense. Operation of both processes may be called *morphogenesis* (the origin of form).

The growth of a higher plant provides an excellent example of growth and differentiation; by cell division the units of its structure are increased, but the units do not all remain alike as the organism matures. Most of them specialize to form certain kinds of cells. Groups

---

* This definition tends to be difficult to apply in some instances, and some prefer to define growth as an increase in protoplasm; but that definition is even more difficult to apply.

of similar or different cells form tissues, groups of tissues form organs, which in turn are aggregated into the plant body or organism (see Fig. 1-4).

Growth processes may be thought of as occurring on three levels— the cell, the organ, and the intact plant.

Growth on the Cellular Level

In a fundamental sense, all plant growth is cellular growth, and there are three aspects to this process which may sometimes be separated in space and in time: cell division, cell enlargement, and cell differentiation. Any sustained biological growth requires at least the first two. Cells have a maximum volume,* and so cell division is a necessity. Yet cell division by itself would result only in smaller and smaller cells—a phenomenon that occurs for a limited time in certain stages of higher plant growth. In organisms that contain more than a single cell type (all those discussed in this volume), the differentiation step is also essential. As a rule, little if any differentiation occurs during cell division itself; it occurs only after cell enlargement is well under way or nearly complete.

In plants, cell enlargement occurs more usually in one dimension than in the others, although initial enlargement following division may take place in all directions. Predominant enlargement in one dimension results in cell elongation, which typifies much of plant growth (parenchyma and other cell types may expand more or less uniformly). We still lack a complete understanding of the physiology of cell elongation, although we now recognize certain chemicals that seem to be in control of the process (see Chapter 8).

One of the most intricate natural sequences of events in nature is the division of the cell nucleus. This was discussed in *The Plant Cell,* and it is difficult to imagine what causal forces might be at work which could result in the series of steps that constitute nuclear division. So far, the biologist is almost at a complete loss to *explain* nuclear division, although it is one of the *best-described* processes in biology.

In many instances the nucleus can divide without an accompanying division of the cytoplasm. In other instances cell walls are formed, causing a division of the cytoplasm even though nuclear division does not occur. Hence, these two processes may be considered separately.

Growth at the Organ Level

The growth of an organ with its various tissues seems to constitute an order of complexity not contained in the discussion of cellular

---

* Perhaps governed by the volume-surface relationship: as volume increases, surface per unit volume decreases.

growth above. In organ growth, we are concerned with the enlargement, division, and differentiation of cells occurring at the right *place* and the right *time* to produce the organ in question. There is an integration of many apparently diverse processes, but at present it escapes our understanding. Just how do branch roots, buds, leaves, and flowers form from the main root or the stem? The fact that these organs form from a mass of cells in a tissue culture or a *callus* (tumor-like growth typically on a stem) provides us with an important research tool (see Chapter 6), and the processes have been well described (Chapters 5, 9, 10, and 13), but little is known about the mechanisms involved.

Consideration of growth at the organ level allows one of the really fundamental problems of biology to become apparent. We know from genetics and other evidences (see Chapter 6) that the genes controlling the characteristics of an organism are the same in each cell of the mature plant or animal. Why then do some cells differentiate to produce leaves, others to produce branch roots, and others to produce flowers? It would appear, since the features of these organs are specific for a given species, that certain genes are acting in one case and others are acting in another. Since all of the genes are present in each cell, why should any one set of genes predominate in its activity at any given time?

There are many places to study this fundamental question; one is at the formation of flowers. In certain plants (see Chapter 16), the stems grow vegetatively until some external change takes place in the environment. At this time, the leaf synthesizes a hormone that is subsequently transmitted to the tip of the stem. When it arrives, it seems to redirect the course of the growth process so that flowers are produced instead of leaves. Apparently certain genes are being turned on (activated) and others, perhaps, are being turned off in response to this chemical substance. Knowledge about the manner in which this substance acts would fill an important gap in our understanding of life processes.

Growth in the Intact Plant

Just as the cells, which appear to be independent units, grow and differentiate in an integrated manner, resulting in the formation of an organ, so the growth of the various plant organs is closely correlated. The shoots never completely outgrow the roots, nor do the roots outgrow the shoots. A striking but more subtle correlation is that known as *allometric growth,* in which the relative rates of growth of two different parts of a plant, or two dimensions of a single plant organ

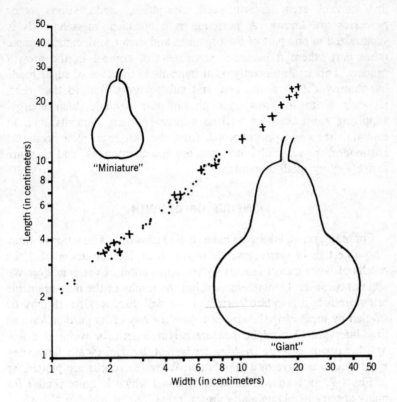

Fig. 4-1. *The relative growth of length to width in bottle gourds—an example of allometric growth. Although width increases more than length, the relative rate is the same in both "miniature" (dots) and "giant" (crosses). From Edmund W. Sinnott,* Plant Morphogenesis (*McGraw-Hill Book Co., Inc., 1960*), *by permission.*

such as a leaf or a fruit, are constant, even though the actual rates of growth in the two cases are quite different (see Fig. 4-1).

How are we to understand these interesting correlations? One obvious explanation is the nutritional one. The growth of the shoot cannot greatly exceed that of the root, since the shoot must obtain water and nutrients from the soil through the roots; and the roots cannot outgrow the shoots, because they must obtain the products of photosynthesis from the shoots. There are many cases, however, when such a simple explanation does not seem to suffice, as in the case of allometry mentioned above.

Another concept that is helpful, but also insufficient in some of the more involved cases, is that of the hormone. We have alluded to chemical substances that control flowering, and similar hormones that control stem growth, cell elongation, and various other processes are known. A hormone is a chemical messenger. It is synthesized in one part of the organism and then translocated to some other part where it exercises some sort of control in the growth process. This is also exactly what happens in the case of sugar made by photosynthesis in the leaf and subsequently sent to the roots, allowing them to grow, but physiologists exclude such energy-supplying substances, as well as mineral-nutrient elements such as calcium, iron, and phosphorous, from the definition of a hormone. Hormones are naturally occurring organic compounds, and they are active in very small amounts.

KINETICS OF GROWTH

For many years, biologists have studied growth as a function of time. The objective in many cases is to try to explain or understand the results of these measurements by the application of mathematics. We will not consider the mathematics, but the results of the measurements often produce a standard curve that we will discuss. Growth may be studied by measuring the size of a plant or any of its parts at various time intervals. One might measure height, length, or width of a leaf or other organ, or even fresh or dry weight, by periodically harvesting plants representative of a population. When the results are plotted, as in Fig. 4-2, an S-shaped curve is obtained which is quite similar for many species of plants and animals, regardless of whether the whole organism or only certain of its parts are measured.

It is important to consider the growth rate, as well as the actual size, at any period of time. The growth rate is measured by determining the change in size over an interval of time. A typical growth rate might be expressed as centimeters per day, or grams of fresh or dry weight per day. The growth rate at any point in time can be determined by measuring the slope of the growth curve. This can be conveniently done by laying a ruler along the curve so that it is exactly tangent to the point under consideration. The slope of the ruler can then be expressed as size increments per unit of time (Fig. 4-2). When the slope of the curve is determined at various points in time, then the results can be plotted to show growth rate as a function of time (broken line in Fig. 4-2). The shape of this curve sometimes resembles the bell-shaped normal distribution curve, but in many cases it is much flatter across the top. Indeed, there are instances in which the shape of both the growth and the rate curves deviates widely from the typical form. The growth curve for the human being is an outstanding case in point.

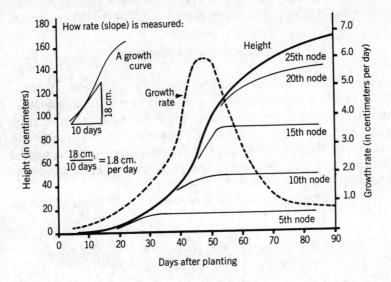

Fig. 4-2. *Some of the kinetics of growth. The solid curve (with points) shows the height of a corn plant as a function of its age after planting. The heights of every fifth node on the plant are also shown, indicating, for example, that the stem below the tenth node is still growing ten days or so after the fifteenth node has been initiated. The broken curve, showing growth rate (unit increase in height per unit time) as a function of age, is derived directly from the solid one. A way of graphically measuring the rate is shown in the upper left corner of the figure. Note that in this plant the maximum rate of growth lasts only a few days (about the 46th to the 51st day). Data reworked from W. Gordon Whaley, "Growth as a General Process,"* Encyclopedia of Plant Physiology, *Vol. 14 (1961), pp. 71–112.*

The S-shaped growth curve can usually be described with reference to three phases. The first phase is called the *logarithmic phase*. During this period of growth, the rate of increase in size is proportional to the size. That is, the larger the organism is, the more it enlarges per unit interval of time. As a result, the size and rate curves have the same form. The second phase is called the *maximum growth phase*. During this period, growth rate is relatively constant and independent of size of the organism. With some species the maximum rate may occur only on one day, in which case it would not be distinguished as a separate phase. In other plants, the maximum rate may be sustained for days or even weeks. Maximum plant-growth rates (heights) may approximate 5 to 10 centimeters per day, but bamboo shoots have been known to grow 60 centimeters (two feet) each day for a number of days! The third phase of growth is called the *senescence phase*. During this period the rate of increase in size becomes less with succeeding intervals until finally there is no further increase in size.

DISTRIBUTION OF GROWTH

Growth is not uniform over the entire plant; if it were, S-shaped curves could not be obtained for individual organs. In the middle of the last century, Julius von Sachs, often called the father of plant physiology, studied the distribution of growth by marking young roots, stems, and leaves with India ink and then observing the subsequent patterns that were produced. Such experiments are illustrated in Fig. 4-3.

In roots, elongation growth occurs primarily in a region just behind

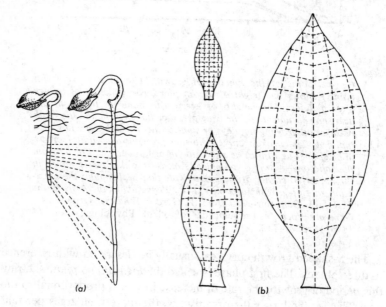

(a)   (b)

Fig. 4-3. *Distribution of growth in* (a) *a growing squash root and* (b) *a tobacco leaf. At the initiation of the experiment, equal distances or equal areas are marked on the root or on the young leaf. After growth has progressed, some of the intervals on the root have elongated much more than others, but the areas on the leaf have remained somewhat constant, although patterns of unequal growth are evident. Fig.* (a) *from Edmund W. Sinnott,* Plant Morphogenesis *(McGraw-Hill Book Co., Inc., 1960), by permission;* (b) *from J. F. Bonner and A. W. Galston,* Principles of Plant Physiology *(San Francisco: W. H. Freeman and Co., 1952). After Avery,* Am. J. Botany, *20, 1933. By permission.*

the root tip. The stem also elongates in a region below the tip, but the height of the tip is determined not only by this elongation but also by growth of the individual internodes below. Dicot leaves typically expand rather uniformly, but the irregularities in their formation and subsequent expansion result in their highly varied form. Grass leaves do not expand uniformly but grow mostly at the base.

Stem elongation ceases completely at some distance below the tip, and thus the trunk of a tree never elongates but only grows in diameter. Nevertheless, stems elongate at much greater distances from the tip than do roots. Only root cells very close to the tip elongate. The reason becomes apparent when one imagines trying to push a thin root through the soil by holding it several inches from the tip! The stem, on the other hand, may elongate for many centimeters below the tip, as is shown by the measurements illustrated in Fig. 4-2.

5

MERISTEMS

Plants, unlike many animals, possess a so-called "open" system of growth. This simply means that plants possess more or less perennially embryonic regions, from which new tissues and organs are periodically produced. Such embryonic regions are referred to as *meristems*. Somewhat more exact definitions have been coined to describe meristems. For example, they have been defined as "perpetually young tissue concerned primarily with growth," and as "regions of more or less continuous cell and tissue initiation." In the vascular plants, some types of meristems arise during the formation of the embryo while other types appear somewhat later in the development of the organism.

APICAL AND LATERAL MERISTEMS

The first meristems to appear during the development of the vegetative body of a vascular plant are located at the tips of the embryonic root and the embryonic shoot. These meristems, due to their location, are referred to as *apical meristems*. All of the *primary meristematic tissues* and hence all of the *primary tissues* of the plant body originate from either the root apical meristem or the shoot apical meristem.

In many types of plants—principally *herbaceous* forms (that is, plants with a limited amount of woody tissue)—the *only* meristems present are apical meristems. Hence, in such cases the mature plant body is made up of primary tissues. The root apical meristem produces the primary tissues composing the mature herbaceous root; the shoot apical meristem produces the primary tissues composing the mature herbaceous stem and the primary tissues making up the mature leaf.

Often, in addition to the apical meristems of the root and shoot, there are present in the vegetative plant body *lateral meristems,* named the *vascular cambium* and the *cork cambium*. Activity of lateral meristems results in the formation of *secondary tissues*. The vegetative plant body of a typical woody organism is made up of both primary and secondary tissues. Growth in length of a vegetative organ is a function of the apical meristem; growth in diameter (over and above the diameter attained as a result of primary growth) is a function of the lateral meristem of that organ.

Some plants, such as grasses, possess *intercalary meristems*. These growth regions may be interpreted as areas of rapid but limited growth occurring between zones of differentiated primary tissue. In the grasses, such intercalary meristems are located at the bases of young leaves and young internodal regions. After maturation of the leaves and the internodal regions, the intercalary meristems gradually lose their ability to produce new cells and then differentiate into primary tissue.

Meristematic cells often differ cytologically to a considerable degree when compared with cells from mature differentiated tissue. The classical meristematic cell from a root or shoot apex is one with very thin primary walls, dense cytoplasm, a large nucleus, small, dispersed vacuoles, no well-developed plastids (proplastids are usually present), and a poorly developed endoplasmic reticulum. Intercellular spaces are also usually lacking. No single type of meristematic cell possesses *all* of these characteristics. For example, in gymnosperms the initials of the shoot apical meristem are relatively large, vacuolate cells with thickened cell walls.

The plane of division of a given cell or of all the cells composing a meristem is of importance in determining growth patterns in a given tissue or organ. Often in describing the type of cell division that occurs during the growth of the stem or root, the surface of the organ is used as a reference point (see Fig. 5-1). A division plane parallel to the surface is referred to as *periclinal,* whereas one at right angles to the surface is termed *anticlinal.* A division occurring at right angles to the long axis of a cylindrical organ is referred to as *transverse.*

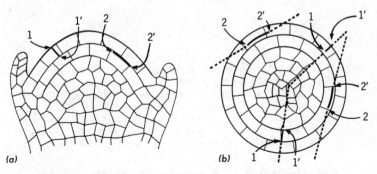

(a)   (b)

Fig. 5-1. (a) *Diagram of a median longitudinal section of a shoot apical meristem showing anticlinal (1–1') and periclinal (2–2') planes of division. (b) Cross-sectional diagram of a stem or root showing radial (1–1') and tangential (2–2') planes of division.*

Two types of divisions that are parallel with the long axis are possible: one, called *radial* occurs parallel with a radius of the circle making up the short axis, and the other, called *tangential,* occurs at right angles to the radius. These terms (transverse, radial, and tangential) are also used to describe sections or cuts through vegetative organs or tissues in planes corresponding to the planes of division just described.

If cell division in a given meristem is limited to a single plane, such a meristem is referred to as a *rib* or *file meristem,* and longitudinal rows of cells are produced. If cell division is limited to two planes, a *plate meristem* is involved and an essentially flat tissue or organ such as a leaf is produced. Cell division occurring in all planes is a feature of the *mass meristem,* resulting in the formation of a massive plant body or organ.

ORGANIZATION OF APICAL MERISTEMS

The apical meristems produce, through cell division, primary meristematic tissues that in turn differentiate into mature primary tissues. In many of the ferns, horsetails, and club mosses, the apical meristem of a shoot or a root is organized around an apical cell. Such apical cells were recognized and correctly interpreted as being the center of the structure and growth as early as 1878. Several types of apical cells are recognized in the lower vascular plants (see Fig. 5-2a):

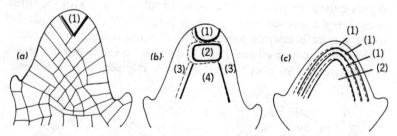

Fig. 5-2. (*a*) *Diagram of the shoot apex of a lower vascular plant* (Equisetum *spp*) *showing a single tetrahedral apical cell* (*1*). (*b*) *Diagram of the shoot apex of a gymnosperm* (Abies *spp*) *illustrating cytohistological zonation.* (*1*) *Zone of apical initials.* (*2*) *Mother cell zone.* (*3*) *Peripheral zone.* (*4*) *Pith rib meristem.* (*c*) *Diagram of the shoot apex of a dicotyledon showing tunica-corpus organization.* (*1*) *Various tunica layers.* (*2*) *Corpus.*

1. *The "Three-Sided" or Tetrahedral Apical Cell* (the fourth surface is the base). In shoot apical meristems, the apex of the tetrahedron is oriented away from the surface toward the base of the shoot. Cell divisions oriented parallel with the base do not occur, but

rather the planes of division occur parallel to the sides of the apical cell. In root apical meristems, the base of the apical cell is oriented towards the root tip. Cell divisions occur parallel with the three sides and the base (base divisions produce the root cap).

2. *The Lenticular Apical Cell.* This type of two-sided cell is found only in the shoots and leaves of lower vascular plants. It is shaped like a double convex lens. Cell division occurs alternately, parallel with first one surface and then the other.

3. *Four-Sided or Pentahedral Apical Cells and Many-Sided or Polyhedral Apical Cells.* These types also occur, but they are not so common as the tetrahedral and lenticular types.

Apical cells are not known to occur in the seed plants. Rather, the apical meristems of higher plants are made up of a variable number of cells with differing cytologic characteristics and relatively complex organizational patterns. Several theories have been proposed to explain the organization and activity of these shoot apical meristems (see Fig. 5-2).

The *histogen theory,* formulated by Hanstein in 1868, states that the plant body has its origin in a terminal meristem made up of three zones or histogens: the *dermatogen,* giving rise to the *epidermis;* the *periblem,* giving rise to the *cortex;* and the *plerome,* giving rise to the *stele.* Furthermore, each histogen has its own *initials.* (Initials may be defined as the cells of the meristem that give rise to new cells and tissues but in themselves remain as a part of the meristem.) This theory has application in the study of root development, but is of little value in describing shoot development since, in most cases, no definite histogens *or* groups of initials related directly to primary tissues exist.

A theory that has received a great deal of favorable comment, and one that is utilized generally to describe organization in the shoot apical meristems of flowering plants, is the *tunica-corpus theory* (see Figs. 5-2c and 5-3). According to this view, two tissue zones occur in shoot apical meristems: the *tunica,* consisting of one or more peripheral layers of cells, and the *corpus,* a central group of cells enclosed by the tunica. The tunica layer or layers is differentiated from the corpus in that the cells of the tunica divide *only* in an anticlinal plane (at right angles to the surface of the meristem). The cells of the corpus divide anticlinally, periclinally, and obliquely. Each tunica layer has its own initials, and the corpus has one layer of initials.

In basic contrast to the histogen theory, the tunica-corpus theory does not imply any relationship between apical zonation and sub-

Leaf primordia

Corpus

Tunica
layers

Leaf primordia

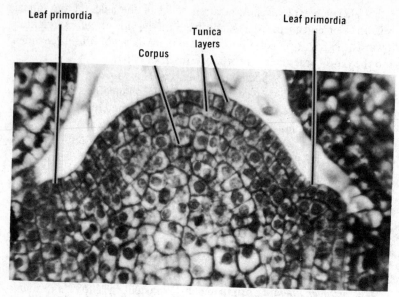

Fig. 5-3. *Median longitudinal section through the shoot tip of* Coleus, *a dicotyledon, showing tunica-corpus organization and leaf primordia.* × *450 (magnified 450 times).*

sequent formation of tissues. Tunica-corpus organization is a feature of dicotyledonous and monocotyledonous apexes. Some gymnosperms (*Ephedra, Gnetum*) also show this type of apical arrangement. However, in the great majority of gymnosperms that have been investigated, no tunica-corpus organization is evident. These gymnosperms possess apexes made up of several rather distinct regions, defined as cytohistological zones (see Fig. 5-2b).

The apical meristem of the root differs from that of the shoot in several respects. First, it is protected by and partly enclosed within a mature, fully differentiated structure, the *root cap*. Second, it does not directly give rise to any lateral appendages comparable to leaves. Branch roots have their origin from mature root tissue somewhat removed from the terminal meristem. Root apical meristems, like those of the shoot, are not cytologically homogeneous, but rather are made up of several types of cells, organized in various ways. The root apexes of certain lower vascular plants (*Equisetum,* for example) are organized around a single tetrahedral apical cell. In the seed plants, organization is more complex, involving one to several sets of apical initials. In some of the dicotyledons with three sets of initials, one group produces the central cylinder of the root, one group the cortex, and one group the epidermis and root cap.

LATERAL MERISTEMS

Usually two types of lateral meristems are present; the vascular cambium, which produces secondary xylem (wood) and secondary phloem, and the cork cambium, which produces cork tissue and *phelloderm*.

External cellular derivatives
(secondary xylem or phelloderm)

(Vascular cambium)
Lateral meristem   Cells of the lateral meristem, per se
(Cork cambium)

Internal cellular derivatives
(secondary Xylem or phelloderm)

The vascular cambium originates, in part, from procambial tissue located between the primary xylem and primary phloem. In those dicotyledonous stems that have discrete vascular bundles in the stem as a feature of their anatomy at the end of primary growth, the vascular cambium is initially made up of two parts, the *fascicular cambium* and the *interfascicular cambium*. The fascicular cambium originates from procambial cells in the vascular bundles between the primary xylem and the primary phloem. The interfascicular cambium originates in the parenchyma tissue separating the vascular bundles. The interfascicular cambium and the fascicular cambium together constitute a continuous hollow cylinder of meristematic tissue, one cell thick. This meristem is made up of both elongate and isodiametric cells. Through periclinal or tangential division of the elongate cells, new secondary xylem is formed toward the inside or center of the organ and new secondary phloem is formed toward the outside. The isodiametric cells produce radial rows or groups of cells that constitute the vascular rays. *Xylem rays* are formed on the inside of the vascular cambium, and *phloem rays* are formed on the outside.

PRIMARY MERISTEMATIC TISSUES

In the development of the mature primary plant body from the apical meristems of the shoot and root, three primary meristematic tissues are distinguished: the *protoderm,* the *procambium,* and the *ground meristem.* Primary meristematic tissues may be described as aggregations of partly differentiated but still highly meristematic cells. Such cell groups represent a transitory stage between cells of the apical meristem and mature, differentiated cells of the primary plant body. The protoderm differentiates into the epidermal tissue; the procambium becomes the primary xylem and primary phloem; the ground meristem differentiates into cortex and pith, as summarized in the following diagram.

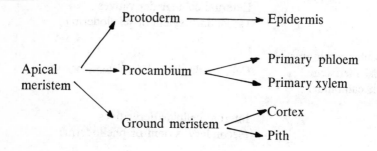

6

DIFFERENTIATION

The descriptions of meristems bring up a number of questions. One wonders why the cells in the meristematic region should be continually dividing while many other tissues of the plant contain cells that divide, at most, only rarely. One wonders why meristems form at various times and places on the plant. One wonders whether a meristem is capable of producing an entire plant, even though it might be separated from the plant that it has already produced. Basically, one wonders how important the environment might be in determining the expression of a meristem's developmental potential. Most of these problems await future research for their solution, but we have fairly complete answers to at least one of them (the third, above) and have made significant headway with the others. In this chapter some of the physiological findings relating to meristems are discussed.

MITOTIC ACTIVITY IN MERISTEMS

One characteristic of the meristematic cells is their position in relation to other cells. Does the geometry of their position at the stem or root tip result in the physical forces that cause cell division? There is some evidence to indicate that such might be the case. For one thing, the formation of the cell walls is often determined by the position of the dividing cell in relation to the meristem as a whole. Cell walls may form predominantly parallel or at right angles to the outside surface of the meristem, for example.

Although geometry seems to play a part in determining the nature of cell division in the meristems, there is evidence that chemicals have an even stronger influence. Furthermore, geometry and chemicals may interact, since concentration gradients of chemicals must arise due to the geometrical shape of the meristem. Plant physiologists are just beginning to look at these interactions between physical form and chemicals. For example, some highly interesting experiments have been done through microsurgery performed on living apical meristems. Most work on differentiation, however, has emphasized the effects of chemicals. We will discuss four lines of research relating to these effects: the auxins, experiments with crown galls, the wound hormones, and work with isolated cultures of plant tissue.

Effects of Auxin

A chemical substance called *auxin* can cause stem cells to elongate (Chapter 8). If auxin is applied to an intact stem at concentrations considerably above those that result in cell elongation, the stem cells begin to divide again, producing a tumor-like growth called a *callus*. Thus auxin is capable of starting one form of meristematic activity.

Crown Galls

It was discovered in 1907 that certain well-known plant tumors were caused by the presence of a bacterium. These tumors or galls usually appeared on the stem near the ground line at the crown, and so they had been called *crown galls*. The bacterium is essential for the formation of the initial tumors, but secondary tumors will arise at different places on the plant even in the absence of the bacterium (malignant animal cancers also produce secondary tumors). Study of the production of secondary tumors indicates that they arise in response to hormone-like materials produced by the primary tumor. Thus we have a second case of tumor growth, which resembles meristematic growth in that there is much cell division, caused by a chemical stimulus.

The Wound Hormone

It has often been noticed that cutting plant tissue (such as a potato tuber) causes cell division a few cells below the cut surface. Cells that have become relatively differentiated begin to divide again, producing a tissue similar to the lateral meristems discussed in Chapter 5, and very similar to the cork cambium described in Chapter 9. If the cut surface of the tissue is washed immediately after cutting, however, then the cork-cambium layers fail to form. It appears that something is washed off that otherwise would have diffused into the tissue, resulting in the formation of a meristem. Long before it had been isolated, this substance was referred to as the *wound hormone,* and the research for it is typical of how such materials are studied.

Although the story is probably more complex than might be indicated here (a number of substances may interact in a series of complex reactions), in two cases, at least, the wound hormone has been isolated and identified. This is done by using the formation of the meristem as an assay for the presence of the material. Washings from the cut surface are applied back to a washed surface, producing the meristem. Such washings may then be fractionated, and individual fractions may be applied back to washed surfaces. The fraction that produces the meristem obviously contains the wound hormone. Successive fractionation may ultimately isolate the material responsible for formation of the meristem.

The work was done first with bean pods, and the material proved to be traumatic acid. The substance is probably different in many other tissues. For example, in potato tissues, in which most of the complications have been studied, one hormone appears to be chlorogenic acid.

Isolated Tissue or Organ Culture

Since the late 1930s, plant physiologists have had a powerful tool at their disposal for the study of cell division and differentiation. This tool consists of growing isolated plant parts on sterile media provided with the essential nutrients. The medium usually contains a sugar such as sucrose and the essential mineral-nutrient elements. Other substances may be added to the medium to produce certain effects, and such additions allow differentiation to be studied. In recent years, two lines of research of this type have produced some important information relating to the causes of cell division: work with *kinetin* and work with coconut milk.

The kinetin work was carried out by Carlos Miller and his associates, under the direction of Folke Skoog, at the University of Wisconsin. They had discovered that pith tissue (parenchymous tissue from the center of the stem) from tobacco would grow on an artificial medium containing sugar, minerals, and auxin, all suspended in a gelatin-like agar. The cells would grow but they failed to divide. Sometimes individual cells would become as large as the head of a pin and could readily be seen with the naked eye. Microscopic examination often showed that nuclear divisions had taken place within the cells, but since no new cell walls were formed, each giant cell might contain a number of nuclei. Miller found that the addition of extracts from herring sperm and yeast would cause the cells to divide, allowing the tissue to grow normally for an indefinite period of time. Pieces could be removed from one culture and transferred to a fresh medium, where they would continue to grow and could be transferred again, and so on. Using as their assay the occurrence of cell wall formation (division of cytoplasm but not necessarily nuclei), they were able to isolate the active material from the extracts. They named their material kinetin, and it proved to be 6N furfuryl adenine. In addition to its effect on cell division (which requires the presence of auxin), kinetin causes a number of interesting responses, some of which are noted below.

Very recently, kinetin-like compounds have been found in a number of higher plants, particularly in young, actively growing tissues. Such compounds may well regulate cell division in normal plant growth.

Skoog and his students had also worked with coconut milk, but the most extensive work with this substance was carried out by a group of researchers at Cornell University under the direction of F. C. Steward. They had found that carrot tissue could be maintained on a standard medium containing auxin, but that the tissue would only approximately double in size, after which growth would cease. Some years before, it had been found that coconut milk would allow isolated embryos from developing seeds to grow on an artificial medium when they otherwise would not do so (see below). Steward found that when coconut milk was added to the medium, the carrot tissue would grow rapidly and extensively for an indefinite time interval.

The problem of discovering the active constituents of coconut milk has proved a difficult one. After failure in many initial attempts to isolate an active fraction from small quantities of coconut milk, the Cornell workers obtained 660 gallons of milk from the coconuts blown down in a Florida hurricane. They extracted from this about 26 pounds of a dark heavy syrup, which they then fractionated into a number of substances, many of which were identified as amino acids or other nutrients.

From this extract, they were successful in obtaining a few purified compounds, which were effective in their bioassay. After further work with extracts from sources other than coconut milk, they concluded that at least three types of substances, all of them acting jointly, are necessary for the growth-promoting activity of coconut milk and comparable substances:

1. *A source of organic nitrogen*—either the amino acids obtained from the coconut milk, or some other source, such as milk protein (casein), that has been hydrolysed into its constituent amino acids.

2. *A neutral fraction* that seems to "stimulate" or "catalyse" the third, active fraction. Such a response is called *synergism* (meaning that the two fractions applied together are more effective than the total activities of the two fractions applied alone). This fraction consists of sugar alcohols such as *d*-sorbitol and mannitol and the alcohols called inositols.

3. *The actual promoters of cell division.* Work on this fraction is still in progress, but a number of very interesting compounds have

been isolated. These all have activity in the carrot assay (provided the neutral fraction is present), but none of them alone or in combination yet matches the activity of the whole coconut milk. One of the active compounds proved to be 1,3-diphenylurea, a surprising discovery since urea and its compounds were thought to be exclusively animal products. Another substance proved to be a colorless relative of the pigments found in flower petals. Other substances have since been at least tentatively identified.

Extracts from many other sources also proved to have activity. Any developing seed that had a liquid form of food storage (endosperm) seemed to have activity. These sources included immature bananas, walnuts, horse chestnuts, and corn; extracts from certain plant tumors were also effective. Potato tissue contains an inhibitor of cell division that seems to antagonize the effects of the promoters. Steward suggests that normal plant growth might result from a balance between inhibitors and promoters of the type he has discovered. Is tumorous growth an instance in which promoters far overshadow the inhibitors?

We should note that both kinetin and the coconut-milk factors cause cell division, although kinetin is only slightly active in the carrot-tissue bioassay. Response is typically a function of the bioassay that is used, and it seems likely that all of the compounds discussed in this section should be considered as members of a single group, the promoters of cell division. Classification within this group will require many more facts.

Most of the cases mentioned above are of relatively disorganized growth, rather than the highly integrated growth that can be observed in the true meristem. The wound meristem is perhaps an exception, and organized growth centers often appear in the callus tissue cultures.

How can we relate tumor or callus growth to the growth of meristems? We have one clue. If a bud containing a normal meristem is grafted onto a mass of callus growing on a culture medium, the callus cells just below the grafted bud differentiate in an organized way so that they resemble the arrangement of cells in a normal stem. A growing meristem, then, seems to be organized in some special way, making it capable of organizing other cells such as those in a callus. The effect can be roughly duplicated by attaching a small source of auxin (such as an agar block containing auxin) onto a callus. It is thus possible that the ability of a meristem to organize cells below may be related to its ability to produce auxin.

Some tumor tissues such as crown gall seem to produce their own auxin when they are cultured; at least, it is not necessary to add auxin to the culture medium to allow optimum growth of these tissues. This is not analogous to production of auxin in an apical meristem, however, since all of the cells produce it. It seems clear that meristems are already well differentiated compared to callus and tumor tissues.

MERISTEM FORMATION

Roots branch by the formation of new meristems in their internal tissues. Indeed, adventitious roots may form on the stem, and adventitious shoots occasionally form from the roots. In the normal development of the embryo, meristems must form initially. What factors cause the formation of stem or root apical meristems?

Horticulturists often propagate plants by keeping the base of a stem cutting moist and allowing roots to form adventitiously on it. Soon after auxin was discovered, it was found that roots may form in the callus tissue normally produced by this substance, especially at the base of a cutting. There is evidence that substances in addition to auxin are required for the formation of roots on cuttings. For example, if a cutting is treated with auxin, and roots are allowed to form, and then if the part of the stem containing the roots is removed, the remaining stem fails to form new roots even though it is treated with auxin in the same manner as was the original cutting. Does this mean that some substance essential for root formation was used up initially and was therefore not available for a second formation of roots? These observations have never been thoroughly investigated, although there is some indication that the essential secondary substance is merely a combination of amino acids and sugars.

It is also possible to study the formation of roots and stem buds with tissue-culture techniques. A certain hybrid of tobacco produces tumors spontaneously on its stem. These tumors are referred to as genetic tumors because they always arise from the hybrid. The tumors can be cultured, and occasionally they will spontaneously produce roots and shoots from the mass of apparently disorganized cells. It was discovered in the 1940s that the number of buds, for shoot formation, was greatly increased when the tissue was grown underneath a liquid medium instead of on top of a semisolid agar medium. Apparently the low oxygen tensions under the surface of the liquid stimulated bud production. After the discovery of kinetin, it was found that the addition of this compound to the medium increased many times the number of buds that were produced, even on a solid medium. Further discoveries showed that the ratio of buds to roots formed on the callus depended on the ratio (not the total amount) of kinetin to auxin: the more kinetin, the more buds, and the more auxin, the more roots.

Kinetin promotes the growth of buds even on the intact plant. In one experiment, the buds grew even when they had been inhibited by applied auxin. In another case, leaf cuttings from an African Violet were induced to form roots by treatment with auxin, after which they were induced to form stems by treatment with kinetin.

How is kinetin acting in these cases? Some indication of its biochemical activity may be implied by its stimulation of protein and ribonucleic-acid synthesis in certain systems. We should expect many interesting developments in this field.

MERISTEM GROWTH

Vegetative growth by apical meristems is an indeterminate form of growth. So long as the meristem remains active, it will continue to produce stem, leaves, and, in the case of root meristems, roots. Thus the plant is a product of its meristems. Experiments were carried out by carefully excising a meristem from an intact plant and transferring it to a culture medium. Would the isolated meristem growing on an artificial medium produce an entire plant or only callus? On the proper medium, even a very small piece of stem or root meristem will grow into a mature stem or root, which in turn will produce adventitious roots or buds and thus a whole plant. The tip of the meristem will succeed in this way, as will a mere pie-shaped segment of this tip. It is interesting to note that other parts of the stem, when transferred to a nutrient medium, often produce nothing but callus. This callus will frequently produce adventitious buds and roots as mentioned above, but the ability of the isolated meristem to continue to produce directly the organized tissues of a mature stem seems to imply some special property of meristems.

MORPHOGENESIS OF SINGLE CELLS

Since each cell contains a full complement of the chromosomes and genes characteristic of the whole plant, each cell should be capable of producing an entire plant. If a cell can produce an entire plant, then the cell is said to be *totipotent*. Obviously, totipotency is not a simple procedure, since excised tissues often grow only into callus; but when buds and roots are induced on this callus, then the totipotent character of the tissue is demonstrated. Is totipotency possible for a single cell as well as a group of cells?

Certain morphological observations relating to the formation of adventitious buds have long supported this idea. With proper treatment, individual cells will become meristematic while still on the plant, producing new stems and ultimately adventitious roots.

Recently the totipotency of individual cells has been elegantly demonstrated. In Steward's laboratory, it was noticed that when carrot-tissue cultures were rotated in a liquid medium (continually aerated and never exposed to gravitational forces coming predominantly from only one side) the medium became milky. Examination of this medium with the microscope indicated that it contained a suspension of individual cells that apparently had broken off from the growing mass of callus. The same procedures also work with other tissues besides carrot.

Given the proper environment, any one of the single cells in the suspension will divide much as a developing zygote does, and will finally produce an entire plant. This finding has been confirmed in other laboratories besides Steward's, including the Institute of Plant Physiology in Moscow. Some of the other work has shown—even more clearly than in Steward's suspension of many single cells—that an individual cell can develop into a whole plant.

These beautiful experiments allow us unequivocably to conclude that the individual cell is totipotent. Yet the importance of the environment in allowing the expression of this totipotency should not be overlooked. When embryos are excised from developing seeds of *Datura* (jimson weed), their future development is strongly dependent on the chemical environment. If the embryo is large enough, it will develop into an entire plant when it is placed on the standard medium. Smaller embryos require, in addition, amino acids and vitamins. Still smaller embryos require all of these things plus coconut milk (it was this observation that led to the discovery of the importance of coconut milk). Still smaller embryos fail to grow on any medium that has yet been artificially provided; but, obviously, the medium provided by surrounding tissues inside the ovary is sufficient. We simply lack complete understanding of the chemical (and physical) nature of this environment.

ENVIRONMENT AND MERISTEM POTENTIAL

Some significant experiments have been done with fern plants, because of their interesting life history, which was summarized in Chapter 1 (see Fig. 1-2). The sporophyte, consisting of root, stems, and leaves (fronds), differs radically in appearance from the small thallus, which constitutes the gametophyte.

Botanists have long wondered why it is that the sporophyte can be so different from the gametophyte. The obvious explanation would be that the sporophyte requires 2N chromosomes in each cell, whereas the gametophyte requires only N chromosomes in each cell. Some early experimental work, however, indicated that this simple explanation was not true. It was possible to observe gametophytes that contained 2N chromosomes in each cell, and even sporophytes that contained N chromosomes. The other explanation that comes to mind is that the spores develop into gametophytes because they are exposed to an outside environment such as the surface of moist soil. The zygote, on the other hand, begins its development into the sporophyte while it is tightly enclosed in the archegonial vase.

Is it possible that the expression of these two radically different growth forms is due to environmental influences? Some initial experiments seem to indicate that this is the case. If the archegonium is cut so that the zygote is not tightly confined, it will often develop into a rather flat, thallus-like body, which, although not identical to the gametophyte thallus, is nevertheless quite similar to it and very different from the normal sporophyte. This experiment, along with the ones summarized above, provides support for the viewpoint that the expression of a developing organism may be radically altered by environmental conditions—either physical or chemical (such as nutritional). But we have known for some time that genes always operate within an environmental situation, and the expression of the character of the gene is often strongly dependent upon the environment.

7

THE PRIMARY

PLANT BODY

The vegetative plant body of higher plants is in general made up of two organ systems, the root system and the shoot system. The vegetative shoot system is further composed of two organs, the stem and the leaf. Stems may be composed entirely of primary tissues (tissues derived directly from the primary meristematic tissues of the shoot tip), or they may be composed of primary tissues and secondary tissues (tissues derived directly from the lateral meristems). Usually, stems composed of primary tissues have only a very limited number of hard, dense cells present and are spoken of as *herbaceous* structures. In contrast, stems made up, in large part, of secondary tissues usually have a considerable number of hard, dense cells and are spoken of as *woody* structures. The herbaceous, dicotyledonous stem will be used as an example in the following discussion of the primary plant body.

EPIDERMIS

The epidermis is derived from the protoderm and is the superficial or outermost cell layer of the stem. This tissue functions primarily as a protective layer and is usually one cell in thickness. Ordinary epidermal cells are living, have relatively thin, primary cell walls, and do not contain chloroplasts (Fig. 7-1a). No intercellular spaces are present between adjacent epidermal cells. The outer tangential and radial walls of epidermal cells are impregnated with a fatty, waxy substance known as *cutin*. In addition, a layer of cutin usually covers the outer surface of the epidermis, forming a *cuticle* (Fig. 7-1b).

In contrast to the ordinary epidermal cells just described, various types of epidermal hairs may also be present, and *guard cells* are of common occurrence. These structures are specialized cells bounding openings in the epidermis. Such openings or pores are termed *stomata*. The size and shape of the stomatal opening is controlled by the two guard cells flanking the stomate. Guard cells, unlike regular epidermal cells, contain chloroplasts and hence are able to carry on photo-

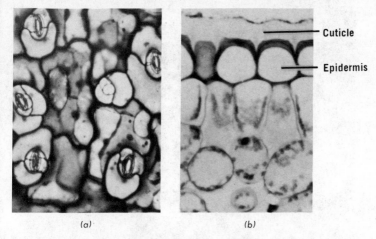

Cuticle

Epidermis

(a)   (b)

Fig. 7-1. (a) *Paradermal view of the epidermis of* Sedum *showing guard cells and in some cases, open stomata.* × *180.* (b) *Cross section of the leaf of* Clivia *showing a thick cuticle on the upper epidermis.* × *345.*

synthesis. Guard cells often have unevenly thickened walls, and are commonly kidney-shaped. Increase in turgor pressure in the pairs of guard cells results in the opening of the pore or stoma between them; decrease in pressure results in closing.

VASCULAR TISSUES

Upon differentiation, the procambium gives rise to the two vascular tissues, primary *phloem* and primary *xylem*. The phloem is involved in transport of elaborated organic compounds in the plant body, whereas water, inorganic salts, and varying amounts of organic material are transported in the xylem tissue.

In some types of herbaceous dicotyledonous stems, the conducting tissues occur as a hollow cylinder composed of discrete *vascular bundles*. Each bundle consists of xylem elements, making up the inner part of the bundle, and phloem elements, making up the outer part of the bundle. Transverse differentiation of a single vascular bundle proceeds as follows (Fig. 7-2): the first phloem element appears at the outer edge of the procambial strand, and subsequent cells differentiate in a centripetal fashion—that is, toward the center of the stem (Fig. 7-3). Conversely, the first xylem element appears at the inner edge of the procambial strand, and subsequent cells differentiate centrifugally, or toward the outside of the stem. If the stem is herbaceous, most if not all of the procambium will differentiate.

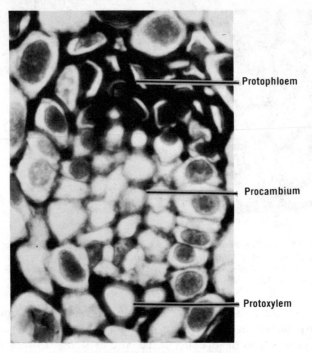

Fig. 7-2. *Cross section of a single differentiating vascular bundle of* Abies concolor *showing protophloem and protoxylem. Surface of stem is at top of figure.* × 800.

Phloem

Phloem tissue usually possesses four types of cells: (1) sieve-tube elements, (2) companion cells, (3) fibers, and (4) parenchyma. The primary activity of the phloem—the transport of elaborated food materials—is carried out by the *sieve-tube elements* (Fig. 7-3). These cells are connected or united end to end, forming cellular aggregations called *sieve tubes*. Sieve-tube elements are unique among living plant cells in that they do not contain nuclei at maturity. The end walls separating two adjacent sieve-tube elements (and certain areas of side walls, also) are specialized as sieve plates. Such specialized walls have groups of openings or pores through which the cytoplasm of adjacent sieve-tube members connect. These pores or perforations are lined with a special carbohydrate, callose. Thus, strands of cytoplasm (called *connecting strands*), passing through the pores or openings in the sieve plate, connect adjacent sieve-tube elements.

When *companion cells* are present, they are usually somewhat smaller than neighboring sieve-tube elements and retain their nuclei at maturity. The presence of numerous small strands of cytoplasm

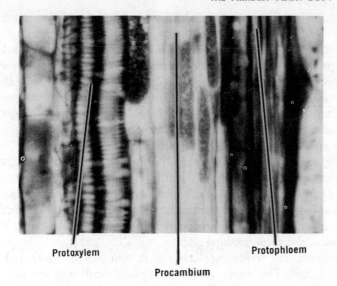

Protoxylem

Protophloem

Procambium

Fig. 7-3. *Median longitudinal section of a single differentiating vascular bundle from the stem of* Abies concolor *showing protophloem and protoxylem. Surface of the stem is toward the right side of the figure.* × *440.*

(called *plasmodesmata* and of much smaller diameter than the connecting strands between sieve-tube elements), which form interconnections between sieve-tube elements and companion cells, lend substance to the belief that the metabolic activities of the sieve-tube element are under the influence of the companion-cell nucleus. Both sieve-tube elements and companion cells have thin primary cell walls composed in part of cellulose and pectic substances (except, of course, for the callose occurring in the sieve plates). Phloem *fibers* are elongated, thick-walled cells that provide mechanical strength to the tissue. Such cells have lignified secondary walls and usually function as dead elements. Interspersed among the sieve-tube elements, companion cells, and fibers are thin-walled, living *parenchyma cells,* carrying on such important activities as food storage and lateral transport of soluble food materials and water.

Xylem

Like the primary phloem, the primary xylem is made up of four types of cells: (1) vessel elements, (2) tracheids, (3) fibers, and (4) parenchyma. Movement of water, organic materials, and inorganic salts occurs mainly in the vessel elements and to a lesser extent in the tracheids.

Vessel elements are united end to end in long rows, forming multi-cellular units termed *vessels*. The xylem of most gymnosperms and lower vascular plants (ferns, horsetails, club mosses, etc.) and of some primitive families of angiosperms lack vessels. Vessel elements at maturity have relatively thin, lignified secondary walls that characteristically have bordered pits. These cells soon lose their protoplasts and function as dead elements. Like the end wall separating two sieve-tube members, the end wall between two vessel members, is highly modified. Such a wall is termed a *perforation plate* (Fig. 7-4). It may be in the form of several or many transverse bars with adjacent openings forming a *scalariform* perforation plate; it may take the form of a slanted end wall bearing many circular openings, thus forming a *foraminate* perforation plate; or it may consist merely of a rim of wall material surrounding a single large opening, thus forming a *simple perforation plate*.

Tracheids, like vessels, are involved in transport of water and inorganic salts. They also perform a mechanical activity, one of strengthening and support. Tracheids are single cells, not linear rows of cells as are vessels. Tracheids have somewhat thickened, lignified secondary walls and upon maturity lose their protoplasts, thus functioning as dead elements. The secondary walls of tracheids characteristically have bordered pits. Xylem fibers and parenchyma cells are, in general, quite similar to their counterparts in the phloem.

GROUND TISSUES

The *cortex* is that tissue located between the epidermis and the ring of vascular bundles. The cortex and the *pith* (the tissue occupying the center of the stem or that region inside the vascular cylinder) are often collectively referred to as constituting the ground system. Both the pith and cortex differentiate from the ground meristem. In general, the cortex consists of parenchyma, collenchyma, and sclerenchyma. *Collenchyma* cells are living, elongated cells with thick primary walls. These cells provide strength and support in young stems and are usually located in the outer cortex adjacent to the epidermis. *Schlerenchyma* is composed of two cell types differentiated from one another on the basis of cell length: elongated elements or *fibers* and isodiametric elements or *sclereids*. Such cells have thick, lignified secondary walls; they function as dead elements and may be found singly or in groups anywhere in the cortex (Fig. 7-4). Parenchyma cells make up much of the cortical tissue, and many large intercellular spaces are evident, particularly in the inner cortex. The pith also is made up predominantly of perenchyma cells. The same is true of the

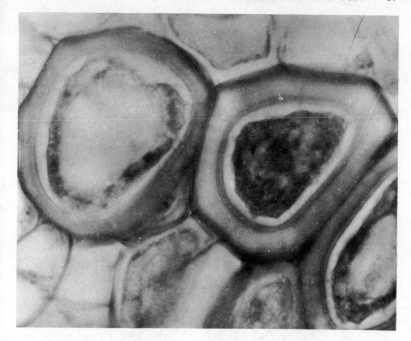

Fig. 7-4. *Sclereids (stone cells) in pear flesh.* × 990.

regions between adjacent vascular bundles, the *medullary rays*. These structures consist of parenchymatous connections between the two ground tissues and provide for lateral transport of liquids and soluble food materials between the cortex and the pith regions of the stem.

THE GENERALIZED DICOTYLEDONOUS STEM

As shown in Fig. 7-5, a generalized herbaceous, dicotyledonous stem lacking lateral meristems would, at maturity, consist of the following tissues.

1. A uniseriate epidermis derived from the protoderm and made up of typical epidermal cells with cutinized walls, guard cells surrounding the stomata, and epidermal hairs. This tissue functions primarily as a protective layer.

2. The cortex, occurring immediately under the epidermis, derived from the ground meristem, and made up of parenchyma cells, collenchyma cells, and sclerenchyma cells. It functions as a food-storage region in lateral transport of inorganic and organic nutrients and water, as a region of mechanical support for other tissues of the axis, and sometimes as a photosynthetic region.

3. The vascular tissues, derived from the procambium and occur-

Epidermis

Cortex

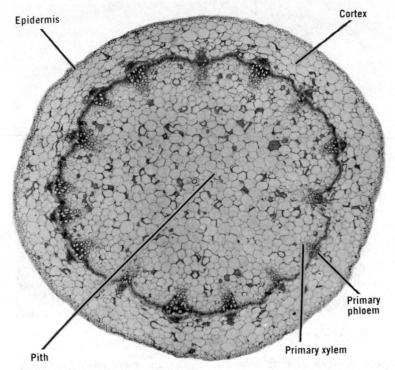

Pith

Primary phloem

Primary xylem

Fig. 7-5. *Cross section of an herbaceous dicotyledonous stem* (Begonia) *with a limited amount of secondary growth.* × *15.*

ring perhaps as discrete strands or bundles made up of two cellular aggregations—the primary phloem and the primary xylem. These tissues are involved in the movement of solutions throughout the plant body.

4. The pith, derived from the ground meristem and made up of parenchyma and sometimes sclerenchyma. It occupies the central region of the stem.

THE MONOCOTYLEDONOUS STEM

If a comparison is made between an herbaceous, dicotyledonous stem, such as has just been described, and an herbaceous, monocotyledonous stem (Fig. 7-6) such as corn, several important differences are immediately apparent. The collateral vascular bundles (primary xylem and primary phloem) in corn are *not* arranged in the form of a hollow cylinder but rather are scattered throughout the internal region of the stem. Furthermore, the individual vascular

Epidermis

Vascular bundle

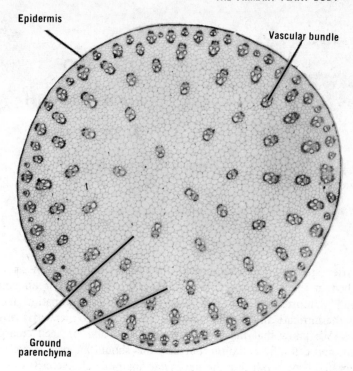

Ground
parenchyma

Fig. 7-6. *Cross section of an herbaceous monocotyledonous stem (corn).* × 15.

strands are enclosed within sclerenchymatous sheaths. Such bundles are termed "*closed*" vascular bundles, in contrast to the "*open*" vascular bundles (bundles lacking a sclerenchyma sheath) of herbaceous, dicotyledonous stems. Since the strands of vascular tissue are not arranged in a uniform, concentric pattern, no clear demarcation between cortex and pith is apparent. In such instances the regions occupied by these two tissues are simply referred to as those making up the fundamental tissue.

8

STEM AND
ROOT GROWTH
IN RESPONSE
TO HORMONES

After studying the anatomy of the dicotyledonous stem as described in the last chapter, you might ask, "How did it all come about?" Unfortunately, we have little physiological information about how the intricate and detailed structures of a mature plant axis originates. We know that the basic pattern is cell division, cell enlargement, and cell differentiation, but why this should happen in such an integrated way, producing the particular anatomic characteristics of a given species, defies explanation. Most work concerned with this problem so far has been confined primarily to the second step in the pattern—cell enlargement or elongation—but work with isolated roots has some implications for growth in general.

ROOT GROWTH HORMONES

One of the earliest discoveries resulting from application of the method of isolated organ culture described in Chapter 6 was that, for continued growth through a number of transfer generations, isolated roots require certain compounds belonging to the B-group of vitamins. This requirement is in addition to the standard sucrose and minerals. All species studied require thiamine, and some species also require niacin and/or pyridoxine. It was further shown that these compounds are normally produced in the shoots and translocated to the roots. Since they are effective in small amounts, they fit the classical definition of a hormone.

These substances might be thought of as cell division or growth factors, since cell division and growth cease when they become limiting in root tissue. It is possible, however, to be more specific than this, since something is known about the usual biochemical role played by each of these compounds. Thiamine, for example, is known to be a part of the coenzymes for the enzymes that evolve carbon dioxide in respiration. It seems quite likely that cell division and growth in root tissue is limited when these compounds aren't present, simply because the biochemical reactions in which they take part are essential to growth of the cell, and root cells, depending upon the species, are apparently unable to synthesize one or more of these compounds.

In this relatively simple case, we probably know more about the actual mode of action of a plant hormone than in any other situation. It is also interesting to note that compounds known as vitamins in animal nutrition may clearly act as hormones in plant growth.

INFLUENCE OF ENVIRONMENT ON GROWTH

Certain aspects of stem and root growth are strongly influenced by environment. If a potted plant is laid on its side, even in the dark, the stem will turn as it grows until the tip is again growing in a vertical direction (see Fig. 8-1). The roots grow in an opposite manner, also

Fig. 8-1. *The geotropic response as illustrated with a small cocklebur plant. The plant was left in the dark except for the fractions of a second when it was illuminated by electronic flash (from one side) for photographing. The response, then, is to gravity, not to light, and the clock shows that it can occur within a relatively short time (very evident after 5 hours and 15 minutes).*

vertically, but toward gravity instead of away from it. Thus the stem is *negatively geotropic* (growing away from gravity) and the roots are *positively geotropic*. Roots, branches, and rhizoids that grow horizontally are said to be *plageotropic*.

If a plant is illuminated from one side, the stem will begin to grow toward the light; illuminated roots grow away from it. Thus the stem is *positively phototropic;* the roots, *negatively phototropic*. There are other comparable responses of plant parts, such as the tendency for leaves to orientate themselves so that they either offer a flat surface to sunlight or are parallel with the sun's rays. Time-lapse photography shows plant stems waving in more or less random motions called *nutations*. These motions in vines cause them to tend to grow around any solid object that they contact.

These are relatively direct responses that can be studied in an experimental way. If these responses in stem and root growth can be understood, then a beginning will have been made in understanding growth in general.

DISCOVERY OF AUXIN

Although space does not allow, it would be interesting to review thoroughly the history of the first discovery of a hormone—auxin—involved in stem growth. Very simple experiments are involved, many of which could be performed on the kitchen table. They are straightforward and in most cases not difficult to interpret. Even so, it required about 50 years (1880 to 1928) for this series of experiments to be completed by workers in many European countries. They could be performed in a few days now, but of course the real problem was thinking of them in the first place.

Early Experiments

Some of these experiments are illustrated in Fig. 8-2. Charles Darwin is credited with one of the first. Darwin, and many scientists following him, used, as an experimental object, the sheath or *coleoptile,* which covers the first emerging leaf of a grass seedling. Growth of this organ is almost exclusively by cell elongation, since most of its cells are formed in the developing seed. Darwin shaded the very tip of the coleoptile with a small cap and then illuminated the seedling from the side. Unshaded coleoptiles bend towards the light, but shaded ones do not. It is easy to see that the actual bending takes place some distance below the tip itself. Since it is the tip that responded to the light, but the stem below that actually bends, it can be postulated that a growth substance produced in the tip becomes

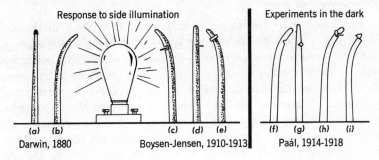

Response to side illumination | Experiments in the dark

(a) (b)   (c) (d) (e)   (f) (g) (h) (i)
Darwin, 1880   Boysen-Jensen, 1910-1913   Paál, 1914-1918

Fig. 8-2. *Some early experiments leading to the discovery of auxin. An oat* (Avena) *coleoptile does not bend toward the light when the extreme tip is shaded* (a), *whereas the control* (b) *does bend. Inserting a small piece of mica in the stem on the light side* (c) *fails to hinder bending, but a similar piece on the dark side* (d) *prevents bending below the mica. Removal of the tip and then replacing it on top of a small slice of gelatin* (e) *fails to stop bending. In the dark, a small piece of stem removed from one side of the coleoptile* (f) *causes bending. If the piece is replaced, or if the cut is filled with gelatin* (g), *bending does not occur. Removing the tip and then replacing it with gelatin on one side and a piece of mica on the other* (h) *causes bending, as does replacing the tip to one side of the coleoptile* (i). *All of the experiments fit the idea that a growth hormone is produced by the tip, and in higher concentrations on the dark side.*

more concentrated on the dark side. This might cause the cells on the dark side to grow more than those on the light side, resulting in curvature. An organic substance produced in small amounts by one part of a plant, or animal, and translocated to another part where it controls growth, is called a hormone (Chapter 3). Thus we can postulate a hormone to explain the results of Darwin's experiment.

This is not the only possible explanation. One might imagine that there is some sort of nervous impulse or electrical stimulus, originating in the tip, which causes the cells on the dark side to grow more than those on the light side. P. Boysen-Jensen, in Denmark, showed that a coleoptile would still respond to lateral light, even if its tip were removed and separated from the rest of the coleoptile by a thin layer of gelatin. It may be possible for an electrical or nervous impulse to pass through gelatin, but it does not seem likely. The chemical idea was clearly the best one to explain these results. A. Paál, in Hungary, caused a coleoptile to bend, even though it was kept in the dark all the time, by cutting the tip off and then replacing it again, slightly to one side. That side would always grow the most, resulting in curvature of the coleoptile. This idea also fits the growth-hormone explanation but does not rigorously prove it.

Experiments of Went

The conclusive experiments were those of Frits Went in Holland. Went was a graduate student working in his father's laboratory of plant physiology. He was serving in the military at the time, but he was able to spend evenings and nights working in the laboratory, where there was considerable discussion of the hypothetical stem-growth substance. Went became convinced, by studying the experiments above as well as many others, that such a substance did exist and that the electrical or nervous explanations were not adequate. Many of his fellow graduate students were equally converted to the idea of a physical impulse. In the heat of one of their arguments, Went said, "Very well, I'll prove to you that the growth substance exists." And he did.

His experiment consisted essentially of a combination of the experiments of Boysen-Jensen and of Paál. The procedure is illustrated in Fig. 8-3. Went removed the tip from a coleoptile, placed it on a small block of gelatin, and, after a period of time (an hour, for example), discarded the tip and placed the small block of gelatin onto a coleoptile that had been decapitated and prepared in the manner illustrated. All of this was carried out in the dark or under a dim red light, which was known to have no effect upon bending of the coleoptile. As in Paál's experiment, when the gelatin was placed on one side of the coleoptile, the cells below grew more than those on the other side, and curvature resulted.

It is extremely improbable that an electrical or nervous impulse might exist in a block of gelatin that has been completely separated from the coleoptile. The chemical explanation, however, fits very well.

Initially, Went had considerable difficulty in making his experiment work, simply because it is not easy to maintain small blocks of gelatin. They dry out if the humidity is too low, or they dissolve in water absorbed from air that is too moist, or they become infested with bacteria if conditions are not sterile. After a few weeks of perfecting his techniques, however, Went's experiment finally worked, and on April 17, 1926, he ran home at 3:00 in the morning to wake his father and tell him that the experiment had succeeded. His father was interested, but commented that if the coleoptile bent at 3:00 A.M., it would also bend the next day.

Went called the growth substance *auxin,* and we now loosely define an auxin as any substance that is active in Went's curvature test and in other related tests.

Went performed a number of other experiments within the next few weeks after his initial discovery. In one of these, he showed that

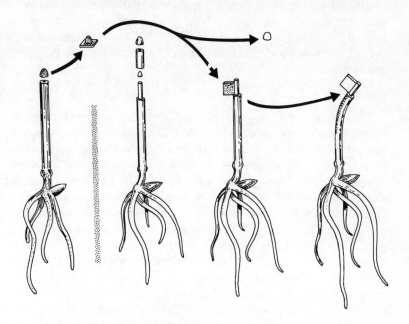

Fig. 8-3. *The experiment performed by Frits Went to demonstrate the presence of auxin in the tip of an oat seedling. The auxin is schematically indicated by stipling. The tip is removed and placed on a block of gelatin. Auxin moves into the gelatin. Another seedling is prepared by removing the tip, waiting a short period of time, and removing the tip again (a new "physiological tip" sometimes forms). The leaf inside the coleoptile is pulled out and the gelatin block containing the auxin is placed against it. Auxin moves into the coleoptile on one side causing it to bend.*

more auxin could, indeed, be measured on the dark side of a laterally illuminated coleoptile tip than on the light side. He also showed that auxin will move only in a polar direction through coleoptile tissue. That is, it will move only from the tip toward the base, even when the section is inverted so that gravity should cause it to move the other way.

A valuable contribution of Went was the refinement of his curvature experiment into a quantitative test for auxin. The degree of curvature of the coleoptile stem after a given interval of time, at controlled temperature and humidity, is a measure of the amount of auxin in the small block of gelatin. Went was able to show this by allowing a single block of gelatin to be treated with one, two, three, or more different tips showing that bending was proportional (see Fig. 8-5, p. 72).

This demonstration of the growth substance, and provision of a means for measuring it quantitatively, changed the entire course of plant physiological research. Many plant physiologists entered the field of hormones and growth regulators, and today a great deal of our information about plant growth can be traced back to this single experiment.

Isolation of Auxin

The test or assay for the material provided a means to try to isolate it and study its chemistry. It was eventually shown that the amount of growth substance produced in a coleoptile tip was extremely slight, and no one has yet been able to isolate any weighable amount of auxin from the coleoptile tip itself. It has been calculated that 20,000 tons of tips would be required to obtain one gram of pure auxin. On the other hand, other sources could be used, and, in the mid-1930s, fractions of plant extracts showing auxin activity were purified and chemically identified. Since then, auxin has been demonstrated in various ways in many plant tissues. One chemical substance, indoleacetic acid (IAA), seems to be an extremely active auxin. This compound had been isolated from urine in the latter part of the last century, but it was only in the 1930s that it was shown to have powerful auxin activity. IAA, or its near relatives, can be found in a number of plant tissues, but there is reason to believe that IAA is not the only auxin occurring in higher plants. A number of relatives of indoleacetic acid are also active, and various active substances have been found in plants which seem to bear no chemical relationship to indoleacetic acid. Most of these have never been clearly identified, primarily because they usually occur in extremely small amounts.

AUXIN IN PHOTOTROPISM AND GEOTROPISM

As mentioned above, Frits Went showed that phototropism could be explained by the distribution of auxin in response to unilateral light. We have yet to discover, however, how the auxin is redistributed in response to light. Does the light destroy auxin or inhibit its synthesis? Or is auxin moved in some way away from the light? It is even possible that an auxin precursor is moved in response to the light. Definitive answers to these problems are still being sought. One approach is to study the kinds of light that cause phototropism. The method is illustrated in Fig. 8-4, which indicates that the coleoptile will bend only in response to blue light. Some compound that absorbs blue light must ultimately be able to act on the distribution of auxin. Since it absorbs blue light, the compound must be a yellow one, and riboflavin or carotene have been suggested. At present it seems pos-

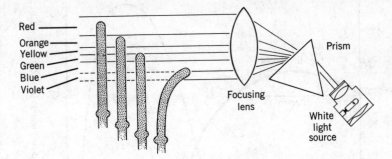

Fig. 8-4. *A schematic indication of the manner in which an action spectrum might be obtained. In the phototropic response illustrated here, coleoptile tips are illuminated with light from different parts of the spectrum, but only blue light causes bending.*

sible that both might take part in phototropism, but definite conclusions await future research (see Fig. 14-1, page 130).

Herman Dolk, working in the laboratory where Went originally discovered auxin, performed the first experiment to show that geotropism can also be explained by auxin distribution. He measured the amount of auxin on the lower side of a horizontally placed coleoptile compared to the upper side and found that there was, indeed, more on the lower side. Again the response to gravity occurs in the tip, and again we are at a complete loss for an explanation. Comparable results were subsequently obtained with true stems. Compounds with molecular weights in the neighborhood of 100 to 300, such as indoleacetic acid, must exist in true solution and do not therefore respond to gravity. There must be some "statocyst," large enough to respond to gravity (larger than a colloidal particle and thus visible in the light microscope), that in some way controls the distribution of auxin in the stem.

Another question concerns the response of roots, which is opposite to that of stems. Does auxin move toward the light and away from gravity in roots? Probably not. It seems more likely that auxin *inhibits* the elongation of root cells (see Fig. 8-5), but moves the same way in response to light or gravity. It is possible that root tissues already contain a saturating amount of auxin, so that *decreasing* its concentration promotes cell growth. It is also possible that root growth is controlled by substances other than auxin. For example, unsaturated lactones, such as coumarin or scopoletin, occur in some roots at concentrations that increase with distance behind the tip. Just at the point where cell elongation ceases, the concentration reaches that which is inhibitory to root-cell elongation when applied externally.

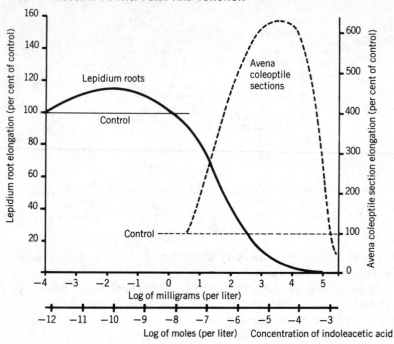

Fig. 8-5. *Growth of roots or coleoptile sections as a function of auxin concentration of the solution with which seedlings or sections are treated. Note that inhibition of root growth occurs at concentrations that maximally promote stem growth. Data reworked from Paul Larson, "Biological Determination of Natural Auxins,"* Encyclopedia of Plant Physiology, *Vol. 14 (1961), pp. 521–582.*

AUXIN IN OTHER PLANT RESPONSES

In addition to the explanation provided for phototropism and geotropism, it was found that auxin would influence many other aspects of plant growth. After the discovery of indoleacetic acid as an active auxin, it became possible to apply auxin in any quantity to the various parts of a plant and study the responses.

Auxin and Callus and Adventitious Roots

Relatively high concentrations of auxin applied to a stem often resulted in the formation of callus and then adventitious roots. Does this mean that adventitious roots are normally formed in response to auxin within the plant? Perhaps, although it seems likely that other complicating factors may also be present which are in some way upset by the relatively high concentrations of auxin used to produce adventitious roots (see Chapter 6).

The effects of auxin on callus formation implies that auxin may, at appropriate concentrations, induce cells to divide. There is now considerable evidence to support this. It has been shown, for example, that normal cambial activity may be under the control of auxin.

Auxin and Lateral Buds

Gardeners have probably always known that when the terminal bud of the stem is removed, the lateral buds immediately become active (or more active), resulting in an increased branching. It was shown with some species in the 1930s that if auxin, dissolved in a lanolin paste, was applied to the cut stump after the terminal bud was removed, the lateral buds remained dormant, much as they would have if the apical bud had not been removed. Does this mean that lateral buds normally are inhibited by the terminal buds because the terminal buds produce auxin? Probably in many cases, but in some cases the story is again undoubtedly more complex. Activity of the lateral buds in cocklebur, for example, is controlled by the very young leaves at the tip rather than by the apical bud. Light conditions (see Chapter 14) applied to these leaves determine the activity of the lateral buds. Furthermore, if one removes the tip, including the young leaves, of a cocklebur stem, applied auxin will not inhibit growth of the lateral buds as it does in other plants.

Auxin and Abscission

If the blade of a *Coleus* leaf is removed, the petiole will not remain on the plant very long. An *abscission layer* of cells begins to form where the petiole joins the stem, and eventually the petiole is separated from the stem by this layer of cells (Fig. 8-6). Yet if auxin in lanolin is applied to the cut end of the petiole, the abscission layer fails to form. Does this mean that the abscission layer is normally inhibited by auxin coming from the leaf? Probably, but again the story is complicated. It appears that the growth of the abscission layer is determined by the quantitative relationship between the auxin coming from the leaf blade and the auxin coming from the upper part of the stem. When the amount of auxin coming from the leaf blade predominates, formation of the abscission layer is inhibited.

At any rate, the observation has practical significance. Spraying orchards with synthetic auxins may prevent abscission of the fruits. Abcission can also be caused, in some cases, with antiauxin compounds. This might be desirable for thinning fruits or in certain crops such as cotton, in which defoliation is essential for the efficient use of mechanical pickers.

Auxin and Fruit Development

It was also discovered in the 1930s that the unpollinated ovary of a tomato flower might develop into a mature tomato fruit when treated

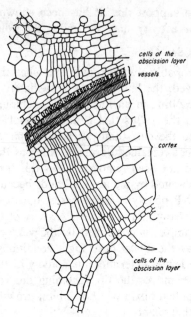

cells of the
abscission layer

vessels

cortex

cells of the
abscission layer

Fig. 8-6. *Formation of the abscission layer at the base of the petiole of a leaf of* Coleus *as shown in vertical section. From B. S. Meyer, D. B. Anderson, and R. H. Böhning,* Introduction to Plant Physiology *(D. Van Nostrand Co., 1960), by permission.*

with auxin dissolved in lanolin. This experiment, and other work, seems to indicate that fruit development occurs in response to auxin produced by the growing pollen tube or by the developing seeds. Immediate practical application of this finding comes to mind. We might, at long last, produce the seedless watermelon! So far, the labor involved makes the undertaking financially unfeasible, but seedless tomatoes are sometimes produced in this way on a commercial scale simply by spraying the entire plant with auxin or related compounds. Seedless fruits, such as oranges and grapes, may develop because they produce auxin in some way other than through the development of the seed. For example, a pollen tube may produce auxin for fruit development but never reach the ovule to carry out fertilization. Fruit development without fertilization or growth of seeds is called *parthenocarpy*.

Auxin and Herbicides

In the 1940s it was found that a new compound, 2,4-dichlorophenoxyacetic acid (2,4-D) would kill certain broadleaf plants (primarily dicots) while not harming narrowleaf plants (primarily monocots). This acid is active in most of the typical auxin tests, such as a straight growth coleoptile section test, but not in the curvature test. Thus the first really important compound in the family of *selective weed killers* was also a member of the family of auxins. Since then, many other compounds have been found to kill weeds. Not all are selective, and 2,4-D is still one of the most valuable. Most of the selective weed killers presently available have no activity as auxins, although a number of relatives of 2,4-D have been produced, and these often do act as auxins. In most cases we know very little about how these compounds carry out their selective herbicidal activity. A great deal of research is going on in agricultural colleges and in the laboratories of chemical companies to try to discover more selective herbicides and to discover the mechanism of action of the ones presently known. For some, mode of action is understood, but for most (including 2,4-D), only unproved hypotheses are available. This is an important modern field of agricultural chemistry which can, in a sense, be traced back to the simple experiment of Frits Went in 1926.

THE GIBBERELLINS

Discovery and Chemistry

At approximately the same time that Frits Went was performing his experiments in Holland, a Japanese plant pathologist, E. Kurosawa, was studying the so-called foolish-seedling disease of rice. This disease is due to a fungal infection, and the symptoms are rapid elongation of the stem, causing the plant to become extremely tall so that it falls over and eventually dies. Kurosawa was able to produce the symptoms of the disease with an extract from the pathogenic fungus. During the 1930s, the active principle was isolated from such an extract and called gibberellin. Considerable study of this material followed its discovery in Japan, but virtually nothing was known of the compound in the Western world. Abstracts describing the Japanese work had appeared in Western journals, but apparently no one had paid much attention to them. In the early 1950s, one group of workers in England and another in the United States finally took cognizance of the Japanese work. They communicated with the Japanese scientists and obtained samples of gibberellin. Within a few years the substance was being produced commercially by pharmaceutical companies. Study immediately became very intensive throughout most of the Western world. The first Western papers appeared in 1954. In 1956 there were 39 papers in the Western world, and only three or four from Japan. In 1957 there were at least 150 papers from the

Western world. The peak was reached around 1959, but research on this chemical is still extremely active.

The chemical structure of the gibberellins has been worked out at the University of Tokyo and at the Butterwick Research Laboratories of the Imperial Chemical Industries in England. Four gibberellins have been extracted from fungal material. They are called gibberellin-1 to gibberellin-4, and abbreviated GA-1 to GA-4. GA-3 was extracted in the largest quantities, and it alone was called gibberellic acid, although virtually all of the presently known gibberellins are acids. The structure of GA-3 is shown in Fig. 8-7. GA-5 was isolated at the beginning

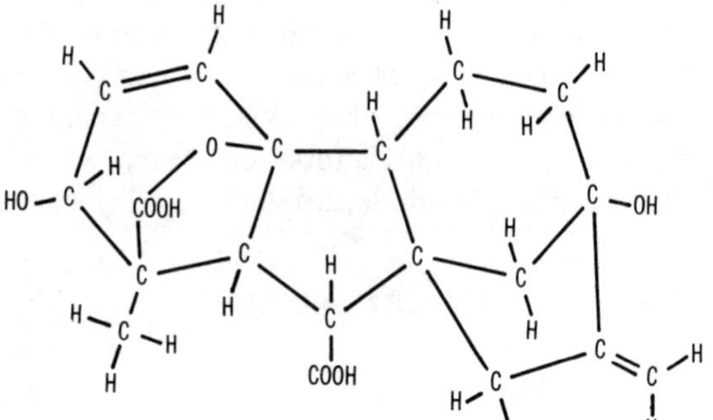

Gibberellin A₃

Fig. 8-7. *Proposed molecular structure of gibberellin A_3 (gibberellic acid). Structures of the other gibberellins differ from GA_3 in positions of double bonds, side groups, etc., but not in basic structure of the three-ring nucleus.*

of the 1960s from bean seeds by workers at the University of California at Los Angeles. Its structure is closely related to the fungal gibberellins. Gibberellins up to GA-9 have now been isolated from various sources. Many other compounds that act like gibberellins have also been found, but as yet they have not been studied enough for determination of structure. They have been obtained from virtually all parts of the vascular plant body, and they occur in concentrations over the extremely wide range of 0.001 to 500.0 micrograms of gibberellins per gram of fresh weight. It seems possible that the gibberellins are of universal occurrence in higher plants.

Gibberellin Effects on Cell Elongation

The most striking effect of the gibberellins is upon stem elongation, as in the foolish-seedling disease. Some plants with stems that normally elongate at a nominal rate will grow six times faster after being treated with gibberellins. Certain dwarf plants will elongate even more rapidly than this, and rosette plants that might not elongate at all often do so after being treated with gibberellins. A few species fail to respond, but they seem to be the exception rather than the rule, and even in these cases a different gibberellin might have produced positive results. It is interesting to note that the response often occurs over an unusually wide range of concentrations. Certain plants that inherit the trait of being dwarfs will grow as well as their normal counterparts if they are treated with gibberellins, suggesting that the normal growth of the plant is dependent upon some naturally produced gibberellin, and that the genetic mutation results in an inability to produce this gibberellin. Finding gibberellins in higher plants supports this conclusion.

Gibberellins and Flowering

One of the most striking responses to the gibberellins is the flowering that occurs in certain plants treated with gibberellins (Fig. 8-8). These plants would normally require either a low temperature treatment or long days, or a combination of both, for flowering (see Chapter 16). Recently it has been shown that such plants contain more natural gibberellins when they flower in response to low temperature or long day than when they are vegetative. This would seem to indicate that flowering in such species is dependent upon formation of gibberellins, although it is also quite possible that other factors are produced as well.

Many of these species are rosette plants when vegetative, sending up a flowering stalk in response to the applied gibberellins. Cell divisions become very frequent as this stalk begins to grow, and thus cell division may be considered as another response to gibberellins that occurs under certain conditions.

Gibberellins and Auxin

Plant physiologists have naturally asked the question: Are the gibberellins a special form of auxin? Since the gibberellins will cause elongation of stems in certain tests that have been used as part of the definition of auxins (see page 68), it would seem that plant physiologists might be forced by their own definitions into the conclusion that the gibberellins are, indeed, auxins. Science is, however, basically more flexible than this. If it does not seem that gibberellins should be called auxins, then the definitions can be altered.

Actually, the responses of higher plants to gibberellins and auxins are, for the most part, quite different. One response they have in common is that of stem-cell elongation. Both auxins and gibberellins

Fig. 8-8. *The effects of cold or gibberellins on the flowering and growth of a cold-requiring plant (carrot, early French forcing). Left: control maintained above 71° C; right: 8 weeks of cold treatment; center: 10 μg of gibberellins daily. The flowering plants are 1 m tall. From Anton Lang,* Proceedings of the National Academy of Science, *Vol. 43 (1957), pp. 709–717, by permission.*

will also cause parthenocarpic fruit development and, in some instances, cell division. On the other hand, there is no polar transport of gibberellin, nor will gibberellins promote root initiation. Gibberellins also fail to delay leaf abcission, inhibit the growth of lateral buds, induce the formation of callus, or promote epinastic responses (abnormal bending of petioles or stems), and often they fail to inhibit root elongation. On the other hand, auxins seldom, if ever, promote the growth of an intact plant. In order to observe growth-promoting responses to auxins, the plant's main source of auxin—for example, the bud—must be removed before auxin application. Gibberellins, on the other hand, will cause striking growth responses on intact plants. Gibberellins also promote seed germination, the breaking of dormancy, and flowering in certain plants, while auxin will not bring about these responses. Thus, while the response that seems most basic is common to both auxins and gibberellins, other responses are quite different in the two cases. It is evident why many workers are rather reluctant to call gibberellins auxins. Yet it is quite likely that the gibberellins do interact with auxins and other growth regulators in many instances.

We will be considerably enlightened in our understanding of plant growth once we have solved the problems that are now apparent in the field of gibberellin research. One aspect has been rather disappointing: the gibberellins seem so far to have only limited application in agriculture. While stem elongation may be sharply increased, the actual fresh or dry weight of the plant seldom increases; the result is tall thin plants instead of short thick ones, but there is no real gain in the amount of material produced. There have been a few exceptions, such as increased growth of celery and tomatoes in some experiments, and perhaps when we learn the proper techniques, we will discover some important agricultural application of these exciting new compounds.

9

THE SECONDARY

PLANT BODY

In many species of angiosperms, and particularly in a majority of the dicotyledons, vegetative growth does not cease with maturation of the primary plant body. In such organisms, lateral meristems differentiate and give rise to secondary tissues. The amount of secondary tissue may be insignificant in the herbaceous forms. It may, in the case of shrubs and trees, eventually make up most of the vegetative plant body, except for the leaves, which are almost always composed of primary tissues only.

THE VASCULAR CAMBIUM

Origin. During growth and differentiation of the primary plant body of a generalized woody dicotyledon, not all of the procambium matures into primary xylem or primary phloem. If, at this stage of growth, the vascular system consists of individual strands separated by medullary rays, each strand will contain, between the primary vascular tissues, a layer of procambium that will become the fascicular part of the vascular cambium (the vascular cambium contained within the vascular bundle). Through the process of differentiation and a resumption of meristematic activity, thin rows of parenchyma in the medullary rays form the interfascicular part of the vascular cambium. The fascicular and interfascicular parts collectively function as a coherent hollow cylinder or meristematic tissue interposed between the xylem and the phloem. It is important to note that this lateral meristem originates, in part, from a mature primary tissue, the parenchyma making up the medullary rays. Such parenchyma differentiates from the ground meristem, the same primary meristematic tissue that gives rise to the cortex and pith (Fig. 9-1).

Structure. The vascular cambium is one cell thick, radially, and is usually composed of two types of elements: *fusiform cambial initials* and *ray initials*. Fusiform initials are elongated cells with pointed

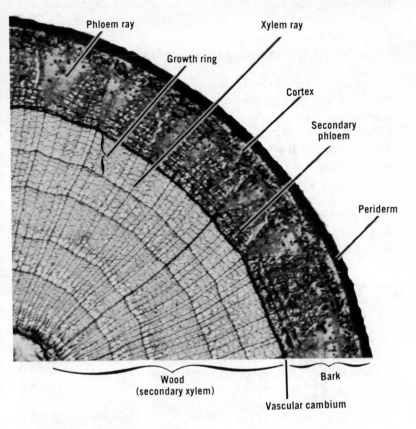

Fig. 9-1. *Cross section of the stem of a woody dicotyledon, basswood* (Tilia americana), *five years old.* × *30.*

ends, whereas ray initials are essentially isodiametric, with a somewhat flattened radial axis.

Activity. Cells of the vascular cambium divide most often in a tangential plane (see Chapter 5 for a discussion of patterns and planes of cell division in meristems), producing secondary phloem on the outside and secondary xylem on the inside. The fusiform initials produce the elongated cell types making up the secondary phloem (sieve-tube elements, companion cells, fibers, elongate parenchyma cells) and the elongated cell types making up the secondary xylem (vessel elements, tracheids, fibers, and elongate parenchyma cells). Thus the cells of the secondary xylem and phloem derived from the fusiform initials constitute the vertical system. On the other hand, the ray initials produce radial rows of isodiametric cells, usually parenchyma, that make up the vascular rays and hence constitute the horizontal system.

THE SECONDARY VASCULAR TISSUES

Probably the most significant single difference between the primary and secondary vascular tissues is their method of origin. Also, differences in cell length of the various elements of the vertical system are often noted. For example, tracheids and vessel elements of the primary xylem are generally longer than their counterparts in the secondary xylem.

Secondary xylem or wood. Secondary xylem may also be termed *wood*. Two different types of wood are generally recognized—*softwood* and *hardwood*. Softwoods are those woods obtained from gymnosperms or conifers such as pine, redwood, spruce, and fir (Fig. 9-2). On the other hand, hardwoods are obtained from angiosperms

(a)   (b)   (c)

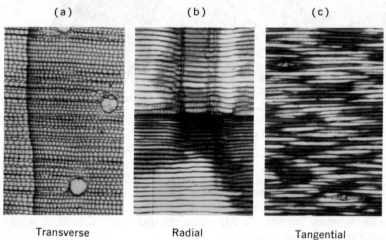

Transverse   Radial   Tangential

Fig. 9-2. *Transverse, radial, and tangential sections of white pine wood.* × *30.*

such as oak, elm, birch, and maple (Fig. 9-3). To assign the term "softwood" or "hardwood" to a specific taxonomic category of plants —that is, to refer to all members of the subclass Gymnospermidae as "softwoods" or to all members of the subclass Angiospermidae as "hardwoods"—is, of course, scientifically inaccurate. From the standpoint of physical hardness or softness, there are a number of woods—balsa for example—obtained from angiosperms that are considerably softer than most gymnosperm wood. Conversely, some woods obtained from gymnosperms, such as desert juniper, are quite hard.

(a)   (b)   (c)

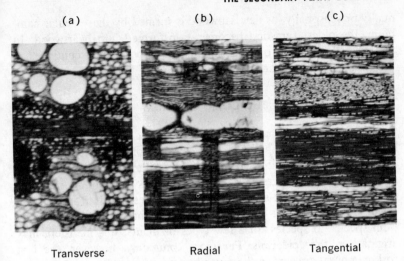

Transverse   Radial   Tangential

Fig. 9-3. *Transverse, radial, and tangential sections of oak wood.* × 30.

Annual growth pattern. In most of the temperate regions of the world, and to a lesser extent in the tropics, woody plants undergo cyclic growth. That is to say, periods of active growth alternate with periods of slow growth *or* periods of dormancy. As a result, growth rings (see Fig. 9-1) are formed in the secondary xylem and in the secondary phloem. If a single growth ring is formed each year, it is called an *annual ring.* In the case of wood, each growth ring may be subdivided into two parts: (1) the cells formed during the initial period of active growth, or the *earlywood,* and (2) those cells formed later, or the *latewood.* If annual rings are formed, the earlywood is commonly called *springwood* and the latewood is called *summerwood.*

Generally, the latewood is denser and harder than the earlywood. The cells making up the earlywood are often larger and have thinner walls than the cells composing the latewood. Fibers are usually present in larger numbers in the latewood.

Heartwood and sapwood. As a woody stem continues to increase in diameter, due to the activity of the lateral meristems, the living parenchyma cells in the pith, the primary xylem, and the innermost rings of secondary xylem gradually die. The cells of the vertical system in this area of the stem (vessel elements, tracheids, fibers, elongate parenchyma) cease to be active. Often various ergastic substances, such as tannins and crystals, are deposited in these nonfunctional cells. The color of the cells may also be gradually or drastically changed. The center of the stem (except for the pith region) is referred to as *heartwood,* in contrast to the active, functional *sapwood* found outside the heartwood and inside the vascular cambium. Annually or seasonally, as new sapwood is formed by the vascular cambium, the oldest sapwood becomes transformed into heartwood. In this way, the amount of heartwood in the woody stem continues to increase, year after year.

THE CORK CAMBIUM

Origin. At approximately the same time that the vascular cambium becomes differentiated and active, a second lateral meristem, the *cork cambium,* may make its appearance. Many herbaceous dicotyledons may have a vascular cambium but lack a cork cambium. Unlike the vascular cambium, the cork cambium originates wholly from primary tissue. The location of the initial cork cambium varies considerably from species to species. In a few types of plants, this meristem may originate in the epidermis. Far more commonly, however, the first cork cambium appears in the outer cortex. It may also originate in a more deep-seated tissue, such as the inner cortex or the primary phloem.

Structure. Let us assume, as an example, that the first cork cambium will appear in the outer cortex. The living parenchyma and collenchyma cells in this region of the stem resume meristematic activity, resulting in the differentiation of a uniseriate layer (a layer one cell thick radially) of essentially isodiametric cells, dividing primarily in a tangential plane. Such groups of cells may form a continuous ring in the outer cortex, but they more commonly occur as overlapping arcs or plates of meristematic tissue.

Activity. Through tangential division of the cells of the cork cambium, *cork tissue* is formed on the outside in radial rows. Similarly, a parenchyma-like tissue, *phelloderm,* is formed on the inside of the meristem. Like the vascular cambium, the cork cambium is capable of producing differentiated tissue on both the outside and the inside. The cork, cork cambium, and phelloderm collectively make up the *periderm* (see Fig. 9-1).

THE PERIDERM AND BARK

Cork cells function as dead elements. They are usually cuboidal in shape, with a flattened radial axis and with thin secondary walls impregnated with the fatty waxy material *suberin.* Such tissue functions in much the same way as the epidermis. During the early stages of secondary growth, the epidermis is usually ruptured and partially destroyed. The formation of a periderm provides a new and effective protective tissue, the cork layer, that may be continuously renewed by the lateral meristem with which it is associated.

As the stem continues to increase in diameter due to the activity of the vascular cambium, new cork cambia commonly arise successively deeper and deeper in the tissue of the cortex, the primary phloem, and eventually the secondary phloem. Such activity produces a complex of periderm and functional and nonfunctional phloem. This tissue is commonly called *bark* (see Fig. 9-1). The dividing line between bark and wood is the vascular cambium.

Once a layer of cork is formed in any given region of the bark, the tissues outside such a layer die because the cork tissue effectively cuts off the lateral movement of food and water to such tissues. These layers of dead cells, including any cork tissue that may be associated with them, eventually slough off and are lost. Hence, the epidermis, cortex, primary phloem, and much of the nonfunctional secondary phloem of any given stem are eventually cast off. This is definitely not true of the tissues found *inside* the vascular cambium.

WOODY STEM STRUCTURE

Shortly after the beginning of secondary growth, a dicotyledonous stem consists of the following tissues: epidermis, periderm, cortex, primary phloem, a little secondary phloem, vascular cambium, a little secondary xylem, primary xylem, and pith. After secondary growth has proceeded for 25 years, the same stem would consist of periderm, secondary phloem, vascular cambium, a great deal of secondary xylem, primary xylem, and pith. The last two tissues listed are most probably dead and nonfunctional.

10

THE LEAF AND

TRANSPIRATION

The shoot system of higher plants is composed of two vegetative organs, *stems* and *leaves*. Stems are essentially cylindrical, vertically oriented organs. Leaves of angiosperms are flat, horizontally oriented organs. Many common gymnosperms have leaves that are circular or angular in cross section and elongated to form "needles." Leaves originate on the sides or "flanks" of the shoot apical meristem as leaf primordia. Development and maturation of leaves occurs simultaneously with development and maturation of the associated stem, resulting in the formation of an integrated stem leaf complex called the *shoot*.

Leaves are attached to stems at the *nodes*. The intervening stem segment between two successive nodes is an *internode* (see Fig. 1-4, p. 11). If there is but a single leaf per node, the leaf arrangement is *alternate*. Two leaves per node results in *opposite* leaf arrangement, and if there are three or more leaves per node the arrangement is known as *whorled*.

EXTERNAL FORM

Leaves consist morphologically of two parts; the *petiole,* which is usually somewhat cylindrical and stemlike, and the *blade,* which is flattened, with an upper and a lower surface. Leaves without petioles are *sessile* upon the stem. If the blade is a single unit, the leaf is *simple;* if the blade is subdivided into a number of smaller units (leaflets), the leaf is *compound*. The uppermost part of the blade forms the leaf *tip*. The lowermost part of the blade, adjacent to the petiole, forms the leaf *base*. The edge of the blade is the leaf *margin*. (See Fig. 10-1.) Since leaves are often used as a means of identifying certain groups of plants, a rather complex set of terms has been devised to describe the type of tip, base, margin, and over-all shape of any given leaf.

Fig. 10-1. *Dicotyledonous (cocklebur) and monocotyledonous* (Tradescantia) *leaves. ⅔ actual size.*

LEAF ANATOMY

From the standpoint of internal structure, the leaf is made up of essentially the same cell types as the stem. However, since the leaf blade is a much-flattened, horizontally disposed structure, the tissue organization is somewhat different from that of a stem. A generalized dicotyledonous leaf might have the following tissue arrangement. The upper and lower periphery of the leaf consist of uniseriate layers of epidermal cells covered by a *cuticle.* The cuticle on the upper epidermis is often much thicker than that on the lower epidermis. Epidermal hairs and guard cells are common components of leaf epidermal layers. Guard cells, and consequently stomates, are often more numerous in the lower epidermis than in the upper epidermis.

Between the two epidermal layers is located the mesophyll and the vascular tissue. The mesophyll consists of two kinds of parenchyma cells: (1) the *palisade parenchyma,* located immediately under the upper epidermis and consisting of one or two rows of columnar cells loosely packed together with many large intercellular spaces, and

(2) the *spongy parenchyma,* located between the palisade layer and the lower epidermis and consisting of essentially isodiametric parenchyma arranged in a loose, "sponge-like" pattern, again with many large intercellular spaces. It should be emphasized that the pattern of tissue organization in leaves varies tremendously from one plant group to another. Figure 10-2 illustrates the internal anatomy of the leaf.

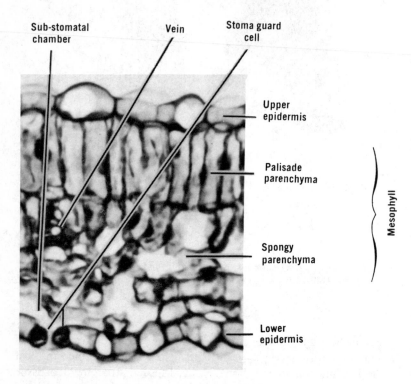

Fig. 10.2. *Cross section of a dicotyledonous leaf* (Syringa vulgaris), *lilac.* × 460.

The vascular tissue, in the form of an elaborate system of *veins* and veinlets, occurs uniformly distributed throughout the mesophyll. The larger veins consist of both xylem and phloem and may be associated with varying amounts of sclerenchyma tissue in the form of fibers. Veins are almost always surrounded by, and enclosed within, sheaths of parenchyma cells. Small veins and veinlets are made up of xylem only, surrounded by *bundle sheaths* of parenchyma. In the case of vein endings, the xylem usually consists of a single tracheid. The pattern of venation in dicotyledonous leaves is commonly *netted,* whereas monocotyledonous leaves exhibit *parallel* venation.

The primary function of a plant leaf appears to be photosynthesis, and all of the leaf's morphology seems well adapted to this function. Its thin, flat structure allows for maximum absorption of light energy. The intricate system of vascular elements furnishes the photosynthesizing cells with water, the essential mineral elements, and special organic materials elaborated in the roots, and removes carbohydrates and other organic products of photosynthesis. The remaining requirement for efficient photosynthesis is an ample supply of carbon dioxide and a mechanism for the removal of oxygen. These needs seem to be adequately met by the system of intercellular spaces, opening to the outside atmosphere through the stomates.

TRANSPIRATION

If the leaf is to exchange carbon dioxide and oxygen efficiently, there must be a large surface area of moist cell walls exposed to the leaf's internal atmosphere. Of course, this will result in evaporation of water from the moist surfaces, and water vapor will pass out through the stomates in the same way that carbon dioxide moves in and oxygen moves out. This process is called *transpiration*—the loss of water from plants by evaporation.

Quantitative ways to measure the amount of transpiration have been developed. Some of these are fairly complex and involve the measurement of humidity before and after a known volume of air is passed over the leaf's surface. A simple method is to use a potted plant, water it, seal the pot and the soil surface—perhaps with aluminum foil—and then weigh the entire potted plant at various intervals, assuming that virtually all of the loss in weight can be accounted for by transpiration. (There will be a small gain in weight due to photosynthesis and a small loss in weight due to respiration, but these are quite insignificant compared to the amount of water lost in transpiration.)

Such quantitative measurements indicate that much more water vapor will pass through the stomates than one might imagine, considering only the area of these small pores. The amount of water typically lost from a plant by transpiration, for example, is about half as much per unit leaf area as the amount of water lost from an equal area of free water surface. Since the area of the stomatal openings is only about one per cent of the leaf area, this is a very striking observation. It implies that gases, including water vapor, carbon dioxide, and oxygen, are able to pass by diffusion through very small pores much more efficiently than might be expected.

The physics of this phenomenon are now fairly well understood, although we shall not undertake any thorough discussion here. Basically, a gas that diffuses through a small pore is very likely to encounter a sharply decreasing concentration gradient of molecules of its own kind (Fig. 10-3), resulting in rapid diffusion (see Chapter 3).

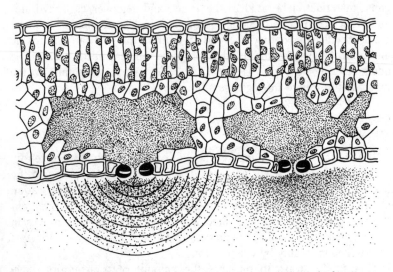

Fig. 10-3. *Diffusion of water vapor (or oxygen) from its high concentration inside the porous regions of the leaf to the lower concentrations in the outside atmosphere. Note the "shells" or "spheres" centering on the stomatal opening.*

Thus, the rate of gas diffusion through pores proves to be more nearly proportional to the perimeter of the pore than to its area.

The ability of the stomates to open and close allows transpiration to be reduced when photosynthesis is not taking place. Thus, in most plants the stomates are open during at least part of the day when photosynthesis can progress efficiently, but they close at night, retarding water loss, although some loss of water does occur by transpiration through the cuticle on the leaf's surface (five to ten per cent of stomatal transpiration). In certain species, such as the succulents that grow in the desert, the mechanism has been even further perfected. Stomates remain open at night when relative humidities are highest and transpiration least. Carbon dioxide is absorbed and converted into organic acids. This requires little energy and progresses efficiently in the dark. The next day the stomates are closed, reducing transpiration during the hot, dry part of the 24-hour cycle. Photosynthetic processes then convert the carbon dioxide fixed in organic acids into carbohydrates and other products of photosynthesis.

TRANSPIRATION AND ENVIRONMENT

Although the study of transpiration as it is affected by environmental conditions has received much attention, many problems in this field remain unsolved. This is because sufficiently accurate investigations have had to wait for development of proper engineering techniques, including the ability to measure environmental factors accurately. Solution of the various problems is difficult and complex because of the manner in which environmental factors interact. A given environmental factor may influence, for example, the opening and closing of stomates, or the rate of evaporation, or the rate of diffusion of gases, including water vapor, from inside the leaf to the outside atmosphere. Furthermore, light commonly influences temperature, and the ability of the air to hold moisture is, in turn, influenced by temperature. Wind movement will both change the temperature of the leaf and influence the diffusion gradients. Thus, the mechanisms of transpiration must be considered as a single integrated problem, and yet initiation into the field is best accomplished by considering the following factors one at a time.

Temperature. There is a direct effect of temperature upon the rate of evaporation of water and upon the rate of diffusion of water vapor, although this latter effect is relatively small. In addition, temperature influences stomatal opening and closing; commonly the stomates close at high temperatures. Recent studies indicate that the transpiration rate is closely correlated with the difference in temperature between the leaf and the surrounding air, when other factors remain constant.

Humidity. The moisture contained in the air in the form of water vapor is referred to as *humidity*. *Absolute humidity* is the actual amount of moisture contained in the air, while *relative humidity* (RH) is the amount of moisture contained in the air at any given temperature compared to the amount of moisture that the air *could* hold at that temperature. Since the amount of moisture that the air can hold approximately doubles with each temperature increase of 10°C (or 20°F), the relative humidity of air at a given absolute humidity will change radically as temperature changes (see Fig. 10-4). Furthermore, the absolute humidity will be radically different at the same relative humidity at different temperatures. Thus the absolute humidity at 50 per cent RH and 10°C is only about half of the absolute humidity at 50 per cent RH and 20°C. About twice as much water can enter the atmosphere at 20°C than at 10°C when the atmosphere is at the same relative humidity at both temperatures. Obviously, absolute or relative humidity data must always include temperature.

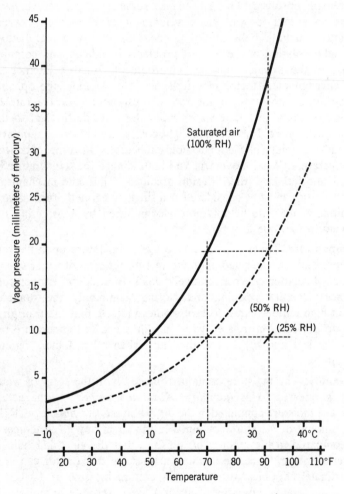

Fig. 10-4. *Vapor pressure of water as a function of temperature (solid line). This is the maximum amount of water vapor held by air at the temperatures shown (or the pressures at which water would boil at the temperatures shown), and thus it represents the vapor pressure of air at 100% relative humidity. The broken line represents half the vapor pressures of the solid line and thus indicates 50% relative humidity. Note that the maximum amount of moisture in air (100% RH) at 10° C is equal to only 50% RH in air at about 22° C and only 25% RH in air at about 33° C. Note that the amount of moisture that can still be taken up by air at 50% RH is much greater at higher temperatures than at lower temperatures.*

Other factors being equal, transpiration will be a function of the amount of water vapor that can be held by air at a given temperature (that is, it will be a function of the vapor-pressure deficit).

Light. Light tends to open the stomates of most plants. Probably just as important, however, is the effect of light upon the temperature of the leaf. Under certain conditions, light intensities approximating full sunlight at noon on a clear day will raise the leaf temperature as much as 20°C above the air temperature. This will, of course, tend greatly to increase the transpiration rate, other factors remaining equal (for example, stomates might close at the higher temperatures).

Wind. Increasing the velocity of air movement over a leaf will tend to remove water vapor as soon as it passes through the stomatal openings and thus produce a sharply decreasing water-vapor concentration gradient from inside to outside. If all other factors are equal, this will tend to increase transpiration rate. Often, however, transpiration rates decrease with increasing wind velocities. In certain instances, this decrease is due to a closure of the stomates in response to the mechanical effects of wind on the leaves and to loss of water from the guard cells by drying.

Another mechanism may be the cooling of the leaf by wind. If the leaf is heated considerably above the air temperature by incoming radiation, wind reduces this temperature difference between the leaf and the air, and, as a result, transpiration decreases markedly. In such a case, transpiration is influenced more by the difference between leaf and air temperature than by the effect of wind upon water-vapor diffusion.

Soil water. When the soil dries out, it becomes increasingly difficult for the plant to remove water from it, and, as a consequence, transpiration often decreases. The guard cells may lose water, resulting in closure of the stomates. Under such conditions, *wilting* may be observed. Wilting will occur at any time when loss of water by transpiration exceeds uptake of water from the soil. Under certain conditions, this may even happen when there is ample soil moisture available. A warm, dry wind on a clear day may fulfill these conditions —for example, the Föhn wind east of the Alps in Europe or the Chinook wind east of the Rockies in North America.

TRANSPIRATION IN THE GROWTH OF THE PLANT

Plant physiologists have long wondered if transpiration benefits the plant in some way or if it arises merely as a compromise with the plant's need to absorb carbon dioxide and give off oxygen during photosynthesis.

It has been suggested that transpiration maintains an optimum turgidity of cells by keeping them from becoming overturgid. Evidence for this viewpoint lies in the fact that plants grown under 100 per cent RH, where transpiration is restricted or slight, appear to be exceptionally flaccid and succulent. Yet they will grow and complete their life cycle, and, while transpiration may be beneficial because it maintains optimum turgidity, it does not seem to be essential.

Transpiration results in a flow of water from the soil to the atmosphere through the xylem elements of the plant's root, stem, and leaves. It has been suggested that this is essential for the movement of minerals from the soil to the leaves. Yet water is used in photosynthesis, and thus there will always be a flow. Indeed, we have reason to believe that there is a form of circulation in the plant (see Chapter 12). The rate at which minerals arrive from the soil in the leaves depends not on the rate of flow of water through the plant anyway, but on the rate at which minerals enter the root. If they are carried in passively from the soil with water, their rate of entry depends on the rate of transpiration; but if their entry is controlled by metabolic processes, their rate of arrival in the leaves is not dependent upon the rate of transpiration. Apparently either mechanism may be important under certain environmental conditions. Sometimes rate of mineral uptake is correlated with transpiration, such as at high soil-moisture content, and other times it is not. Thus transpiration does not appear to be *essential* to the movement of minerals.

Since approximately 600 calories of heat are required to convert one gram of water at room temperature to the vapor state, transpiration acts as a mechanism of heat removal. It has been suggested that this mechanism cools the leaf and prevents damage by high temperatures. Whenever transpiration is occurring, approximately 600 calories per gram of transpired water is removed by this mechanism, but again the picture is complex.

A typical calculation is shown in Table 10-1. The leaf was receiving about 2.1 calories per square centimeter per minute of radiant energy from a light source and from the surroundings. When any leaf reaches temperature equilibrium, received heat must be removed by transpiration, by long wavelength thermal radiation from the leaf, and by conduction and convection to the air. In the case under discussion, about 35 per cent of the heat was removed by transpiration, about 60 per cent by radiation, and about 5 per cent by convection. The main thing, however, is that the heat load on the leaf be removed by these three mechanisms operating together. If transpiration is restricted, the leaf temperature will rise slightly to a new equilibrium level, and the dissipation of heat by radiation and by convection will increase. Thus

Table 10-1

Balance Sheet for Energy Transfer between a Leaf and Its Environment*

	Energy (cal/cm²/min)	Per cent of total
Energy *absorbed* by the leaf:		
1. From the light source.	0.90	43%
2. From the surroundings to the leaf (long-wave thermal radiation).	1.20	57%
Total	2.10	100%
Energy *lost* from the leaf by:		
1. Transpiration.	0.67	32%
2. Thermal radiation *from* the leaf.	1.32	63%
3. Convection.	0.11	5%
Total	2.10	100%

* Modified from data in R. Mellor, F. Salisbury, and K. Raschke, "Leaf Temperatures in Controlled Environments," *Planta,* Vol. 61 (1964), pp. 56–72.

transpiration is not *essential* for the removal of heat from a leaf, because other mechanisms will assume the responsibility if necessary, but when transpiration is occurring, which is virtually all of the time in higher plants (especially when the leaf temperature is considerably above the temperature of the air), a certain amount of the heat will be dissipated by this mechanism. This amount may range from 10 to more than 40 per cent, and is then, under natural conditions, a very significant portion of the total heat dissipated from a leaf.

11

THE ROOT

The root system of vascular plants is typically the underground or subterranean part of the vegetative plant body. This organ is concerned primarily with the activities of absorbing water and mineral nutrients from the soil solution, anchoring the plant firmly in the soil, and storing various elaborated food materials. The root, unlike the stem, does not usually carry on photosynthesis, and has no lateral appendages comparable to leaves.

GENERAL MORPHOLOGY

From the standpoint of external form, root systems are subdivided into two categories; the *taproot system* (common in dicotyledons), consisting of a single large main root, usually vertically oriented with small lateral roots, and the *fibrous root system* (common in monocotyledons), consisting of many individual roots, all about equal in length and diameter, forming a ramifying vertical and horizontal array. Taproots may be quite fleshy and function as important food-storage organs (carrots, beets, turnips, etc.).

Probably in the great majority of cases, the root system is not strictly a taproot or a fibrous root system, but rather falls in between these two, in which case we speak of modified taproot systems, modified fibrous root systems, etc.

The first root to appear in the growth of a plant originates from the radicle (embryonic root) of the seed and is termed the *primary root*. In those plants with taproots, the primary root usually develops into the main or taproot. In plants with fibrous root systems, the primary root is usually short-lived and the various roots making up the system originate from the stem. Roots that have their origin in stem or leaf tissue are termed *adventitious roots*.

A generalized dicotyledonous root, since it is an underground organ specialized for absorption, anchorage, and food storage, is quite different in its structure from a typical dicotyledonous stem. Unlike the stem, in which the apical meristem is truly terminal and superficial on the axis, the root has a subterminal apical meristem that is enclosed within a protective tissue system, the *root cap*. The root tip is subjected to considerable abrasion, since it is constantly penetrating the soil matrix (due to cellular enlargement and elongation in that region of the root behind the apical meristem). The root cap protects the root apical meristem from such injury. The abrasive properties of the soil result in an almost continuous sloughing off of cells on the periphery of the root cap. New root-cap tissue is produced by the apical meristem.

NONWOODY DICOTYLEDONOUS ROOT

Like the terminal meristem of the shoot, the root meristem produces three primary meristematic tissues: the *protoderm,* the *procambium* and the *ground meristem*. The procambium, instead of being in discrete strands, occurs as a solid cylinder in the center of the root in dicotyledonous species. The ground meristem is arranged in a hollow cylinder outside the procambium, and the protoderm is a uniseriate layer on the surface of the young root. Upon further differentiation, the protoderm gives rise to the epidermis, and the ground meristem differentiates into the cortex, including the endodermis—the specialized innermost layer of the cortex (Fig. 11-1). The procambial cylinder differentiates into the primary xylem, the primary phloem, and the *pericycle*—a parenchymatous sheath surrounding the primary vascular tissues.

Epidermis. The root epidermis differs in a number of respects from that of the shoot. Typically, there is no cuticle present on the root epidermis, and root epidermal cells are usually not cutinized. There are no guard cells and hence no stomates in the root epidermis. The epidermal hairs present on roots are in the form of *root hairs,* which are attenuated lateral outgrowths of single root epidermal cells. Each root hair is merely a part of one epidermal cell, not a multicellular organ. The nucleus of an epidermal cell bearing a root hair is usually located near the tip of the hair. The formation of large numbers of root hairs greatly increases the surface area of the root and therefore tremendously increases the efficiency of this organ as an absorbing structure. Typically the root epidermis is one cell thick.

Cortex. The cortex of the root (excluding the endodermis) is composed largely of isodiametric parenchyma cells arranged in a loose aggregation with many large intercellular spaces present. Sometimes fibers, sclereids, or collenchyma cells may also occur in the root cortex. This tissue region is concerned primarily with food storage and lateral movement of water and inorganic mineral nutrients.

In the roots of most higher plants, the innermost layer of the cor-

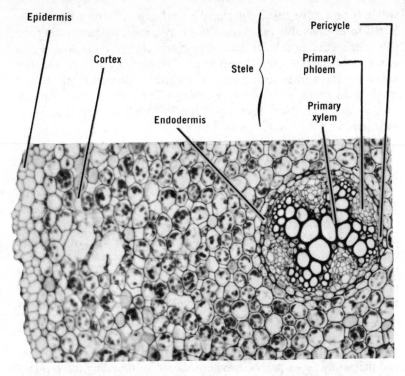

Fig. 11-1. *Cross section of the mature root of buttercup* (Ranunculus *spp*) *a herbaceous dicotyledon.* × 95.

tex is specialized as an endodermis. The cells making up this tissue are characterized by the presence of thin, suberized lamellae (*Casparian strips*) on the radial, upper, and lower walls. The endodermis is one cell thick radially, and there are no intercellular spaces between adjacent endodermal cells.

Stele. All of the tissues inside the endodermis—that is, the pericycle, the primary phloem, and the primary xylem—make up the *stele* or the central cylinder of the root. The pericycle is most often a uniseriate layer of parenchyma-like cells. In those plants with no secondary growth, the pericycle functions only as a place of origin for lateral roots. If lateral meristems differentiate and secondary tissues are formed, the pericycle takes on added significance, since at least a part of the vascular cambium and the entire initial cork cambium originate from this tissue.

The center of a generalized dicotyledonous root is occupied by the primary xylem; no pith is present. The xylem tissue is often fluted, with three, four, or five ridges or ribs consisting of xylem elements running the length of the cylinder. Located in between the ridges are discrete strands of primary phloem. Such an arrangement of primary xylem and phloem is termed *radial,* in contrast to the *collateral* pattern characteristic of the primary vascular tissues of herbaceous dicotyledonous stems (Fig. 11-1).

MONOCOTYLEDONOUS ROOT

Herbaceous monocotyledonous roots such as corn are considerably different than the dicotyledonous root just described, in that a pith is usually present in the monocotyledonous root (see Fig. 11-3). Also,

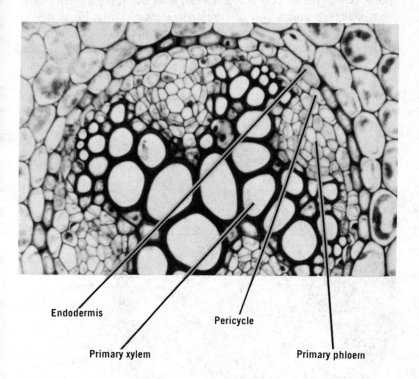

Fig. 11-2. *Cross section of the stele of a mature root of buttercup* (Ranunculus *spp*). × 250.

monocotyledonous roots usually have an exodermis made up of living suberized tissue located immediately under the epidermis. Since such roots have a pith, the primary xylem is in the form of a hollow fluted cylinder with many ridges and many depressions. Each depression has associated with it a strand of primary phloem.

WOODY DICOTYLEDONOUS ROOT

In dicotyledonous roots destined to have secondary vascular tissues, the vascular cambium originates in part from arcs of undifferentiated procambium occurring inside the phloem strands and outside the concavities in the xylem cylinder, and in part from the pericycle in contact with the tips of the xylem ridges. The meristematic cells thus derived make up a lateral meristem that is similar in position (between the primary phloem and xylem) and in activity (formation of secondary xylem and phloem) to the vascular cambium of the shoot.

At approximately the same time that the vascular cambium becomes active, the second lateral meristem of the root, the cork cambium, makes its appearance, differentiating entirely from the pericycle. Once a layer of cork has been formed by the cork cambium, the tissues exterior to this layer usually die. Hence, in the case of roots, the endodermis, cortex, and epidermis are sloughed off as dead tissue soon after the lateral meristems produce their initial increments of secondary tissue. In a perennial woody root, the bark and wood are

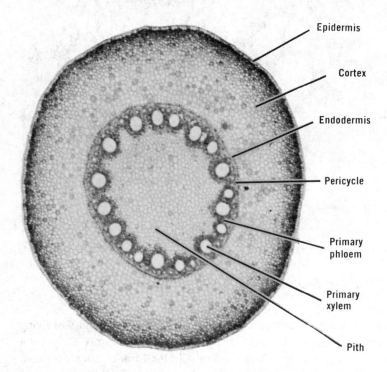

Fig. 11-3. *Cross section of the mature root of a monocotyledon, corn* (Zea mays). × 30.

essentially the same as in a perennial woody stem, except that the root lacks a pith, and the root bark is usually thinner than that of the stem.

LATERAL ROOTS

Lateral roots have their origin in the pericycle of the mature root. Due to divisions in the pericyclic cells, a root apical meristem is organized that produces the tissues of the lateral root (see Fig. 11-4).

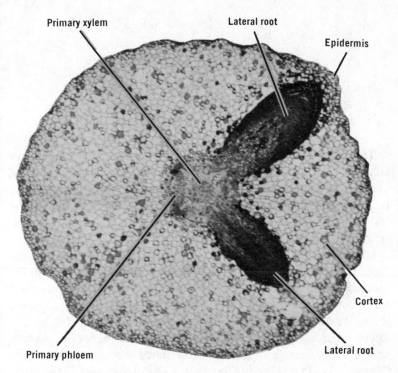

Fig. 11-4. *Cross section of the mature root of willow* (Salix *spp*) *illustrating origin of lateral root.* × *30.*

The lateral root grows through the peripheral tissues of the mature root and penetrates the soil matrix. In contrast to the superficial origin of lateral stems or branches, lateral roots originate in an internal tissue, the pericycle, and, through mechanical force, emerge to the surface of the parent organ.

12

THE ASCENT OF
SAP AND THE
TRANSLOCATION
OF SOLUTES

The higher plant is a dynamic entity. All kinds of organic molecules take part in many complex and integrated chemical reactions. Most of this activity is submicroscopic, but occasionally some functions can be noticed without the use of special observation techniques. The leaf movements that display timing in certain plants are an excellent example (see Chapter 15).

In this chapter we will discuss another example: movement of substances through the plant at speeds that could be noticed with the unaided eye, if it weren't for the fact that most of this movement occurs within the plant structure where it cannot readily be seen. Figure 12-1 illustrates the magnitude of this movement. Of the dissolved substances that are translocated from one part of a plant to another, the flowering hormone may move the most slowly (see Chapter 16). This substance moves at a rate of about six to ten centimeters per day, which is about the speed of the tip of the hour hand on a wrist watch. Most translocation studies have been concerned with the movement of the sugars produced in photosynthesis. Their rate of movement—20 to 100 or even 150 centimeters per hour—is about as fast as the tip of the minute hand on a clock 12 inches in diameter. The rate of water movement upward through the dead xylem elements of a tree trunk may vary from a standstill (during periods of rain, for example), to rates of 50 to 4,360 centimeters per hour, depending upon species and environmental conditions. The maximum rate given in Fig. 12-1 is as fast as the tip of a sweep second hand on a clock 9½ inches in diameter!

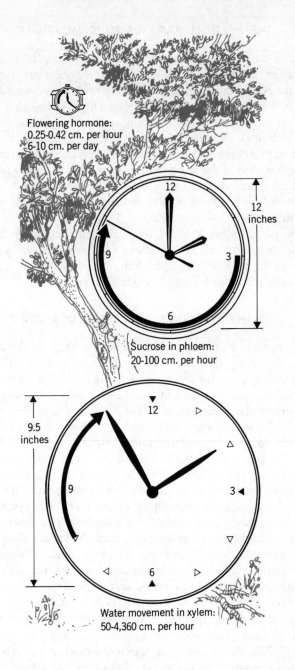

Fig. 12-1. *The rates of movement of various substances within the plant, which vary from 0.25 cm/hour to well over 4,000 cm/hour.*

THE PHYSICAL BASIS OF FLUID MOVEMENT

What is the cause of movement in these examples? Within the plant, or for that matter in any situation where fluids are transported, movement occurs in response to either or both of two kinds of force gradients. First, there are hydrostatic gradients. This kind of force gradient is established in any pumping system, such as the heart. One of the principal theories, discussed below, postulates that translocation in plants occurs in response to such a pressure gradient.

The other kind of force gradient is a gradient in partial molar free energies, as discussed in Chapter 3. Such a gradient results in movement by diffusion, the molecules moving from points of high free energy to points of low free energy.

In the plant, either kind of force gradient may come about in response to environmental conditions (for example, an abundance of water in the soil with very little in the atmosphere) and in response to metabolic processes taking place within the plant.

PLANT STRUCTURE AND TRANSLOCATION

For purposes of this discussion, we may regard the cellular plant body as consisting primarily of two phases, as illustrated. Figure 12-2a shows a cross section of a root. Figure 12-2b shows the cell walls and intercellular spaces of Fig. 12-2a blackened, with all of the living part of the tissue omitted. The system of interconnected cell walls may be referred to as the *apoplast*. Water with its dissolved substances could freely diffuse throughout the apoplast and those intercellular spaces that are filled with water. The water-filled lumens of the xylem elements would also be part of this system. If water and dissolved substances can readily diffuse throughout this system, and less readily into the living part of the plant, this system would be equivalent to the part of the plant called the *free space*. Note in Fig. 12-2b that there is an interruption in the free space along the row of endodermal cells, although this is not a break in the apoplast itself. It comes about because of the relatively waterproof, suberized Casparian strip around each endodermal cell. Thus substances diffusing through the apoplast from the outside cannot pass into the stele by way of the apoplast, but must pass through the living endodermal cells (cytoplasm and perhaps vacuole).

Figure 12-2c shows the cytoplasm and nuclei of the cells in Fig. 12-2a, the continuous living phase of the plant called the *symplast*. Since the cytoplasm is connected from cell to cell by the plasmodesmata, we might imagine that substances in the cytoplasm of one cell

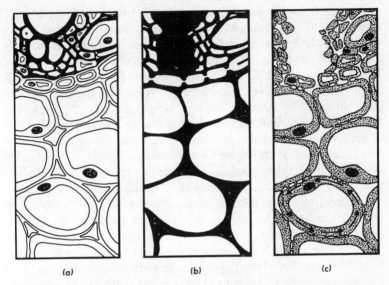

Fig. 12-2. *A way of looking at the structure of a plant, which helps in understanding movement of substances within the plant. (a) Schematic cross section of a root. (b) Apoplast and intercellular spaces of this same cross section. (c) Symplast or living parts of the same cross section.*

could move to the cytoplasm of other cells without ever entering into the apoplast system. They would move only through the symplast. Cytoplasmic streaming would tend to accelerate greatly the movement of dissolved materials throughout the symplast.

The *tonoplast*—that membrane surrounding the vacuole (Fig. 12-2a and c)—is capable of retaining dissolved substances in the vacuole even though their concentration is much higher than it is outside.

ROOT PRESSURES AND EXUDATES

If one cuts off the top of a plant, especially an herbaceous one or a vine such as a grape, material is sometimes exuded under considerable pressure from the cut surface. The concentration of the exuded sap is higher than that of the soil solution (or nutrient culture solution in an artificial situation).

As discussed in Jensen: *The Plant Cell* and briefly mentioned in Chapter 3, the process referred to as accumulation or active uptake uses metabolic energy to move substances across a membrane against a concentration gradient, so that the concentration on one side may build up much above that on the other side.

But how does this work with a whole plant instead of just an individual cell? The apoplast-symplast concept, along with that of the endodermal layer and its impermeable Casparian strips, helps us to formulate a mechanism to account for the observed phenomenon. This was done by Alden Crafts and Theodore Broyer, who, in 1938, postulated that dissolved salts from the soil solution move into the plant primarily by diffusion through the apoplast of the cortex. The symplast then accumulates these ions. Since there is an ample amount of available oxygen in the cells nearest the root surface, they tend to accumulate ions to the highest concentrations. These materials then move via the symplast (undoubtedly aided by cytoplasmic streaming) toward the inside of the root. They have no difficulty in moving across the endodermal cells, because these cells are part of the symplast. Once inside the stele, oxygen tensions are much lower and the processes of accumulation are much less efficient. The substances then begin to leak out into the surrounding apoplast and into the water-filled xylem tubes. Under proper environmental conditions (low transpiration, high soil moisture), this might result in salt concentrations in the stele above those outside of the root.

Such an increase in concentration would then put into effect the processes of osmosis, with the endodermal layer of cells acting as the semipermeable membrane of an osmometer. Water would move in through the outer apoplast, through the endodermis, and finally into the apoplast within the stele. This would create pressure, as in any osmometer, and if the stem were cut, the pressure would be made manifest by an exudate from the xylem cells. Sometimes this exudate appears on the edges of leaves (such as tips of grass blades), being forced by root pressure through small openings in the leaf. This process is called *guttation*.

Thus the structural concepts allow us to account for root pressure. Yet root pressures cannot always be observed. We would expect to find them only under conditions in which water accumulating inside the stele has no place to go, resulting in a buildup of pressures.

THE ASCENT OF SAP AND THE COHESION THEORY

If water is evaporating from the leaves at a fairly rapid rate, we would not expect root pressures to develop at all, and usually they don't. In the absence of root pressures, the plant seems to act simply as a water conduit between the soil and the air; water flows down a free energy gradient, so to speak. The actual movement of water containing dissolved substances through the stem is in response to hydraulic gradients, but these in turn are established by the free energy gradient. The plant is acting like a wick.

Figure 12-3 illustrates this movement of water. In a soil that is

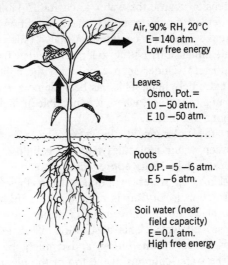

Air, 90% RH, 20°C
E = 140 atm.
Low free energy

Leaves
Osmo. Pot. =
10 −50 atm.
E 10 −50 atm.

Roots
O.P. = 5 −6 atm.
E 5 −6 atm.

Soil water (near
field capacity)
E = 0.1 atm.
High free energy

Fig. 12-3. *Some quantities relating to water and its soil-plant-air pathway. Note that water molecules move from areas of high free energy toward areas of low free energy, but from areas of low enter tendency to areas of high enter tendency.*

wet nearly to field capacity, the osmotic potential of the soil solution is very low, and, if there is no pressure, this potential will be equal to the enter tendency (diffusion pressure deficit—see Chapter 3). The osmotic potential of root cells has been found to be between five and six atmospheres. If they are not under pressure, the enter tendency is from five to six atmospheres, and the free energy is lower than in the surrounding soil water. Free energies are still lower in leaf cells where enter tendencies may be 10 to 50 atmospheres (ignoring pressures), and the free energy of water in the atmosphere is much lower still. In air at 90 per cent relative humidity and 20°C, the enter tendency is 140 atmospheres, and air with a relative humidity of 40 per cent has an enter tendency of 1,220 atmospheres at 20°C. Thus there is a steep gradient from low to high enter tendency and from high to low free energy, going from the soil water through the plant into the atmosphere.

Water readily evaporates from the leaf surfaces (Chapter 10). As water is removed from the leaf, it is pulled up in the xylem elements. The water columns are held together by cohesion—the attraction of like molecules for each other. Rather high tensions may be developed in holding the columns of water together between the roots and the leaves. In a tall tree, we can easily calculate that tensions of at least 20 atmospheres must be developed. Why don't such extreme tensions cause the water to cavitate? That is, why don't bubbles of water vapor form under these conditions, causing the columns to break? Probably cavitation usually fails because of the extremely small dimensions of the xylem elements (from 15 to 500 microns in diameter). Under such conditions, the cohesive forces of water may be extremely high. This has been demonstrated with small capillary tubes in a centrifuge, where it is possible artificially to impose such high tensions in a liquid.

What holds the columns at the top? The adhesive forces of attraction between water molecules and the cellulose cell walls are known to be extremely high, approaching in some systems 1,000 atmospheres. Thus, as water evaporates from these walls in the leaves (the attraction to dry air is even higher), the deficit created is immediately made up by movement of water from the apoplast below into these cell walls. This adsorption of water by materials such as cellulose is called *imbibition,* and it might be said that imbibition holds the water columns at the top of the plant.

There are many unsolved problems in this field. What happens, for example, when water does cavitate in the xylem tubes? This might be expected to happen during a strong wind storm that shakes and bends the tree trunks, and probably it happens every winter in trees that freeze, since freezing forces dissolved air out of the water. Microscopic examination has demonstrated that the xylem elements do contain an abundance of air bubbles after having been frozen. The problems that remain will be solved as we approach them using techniques and knowledge developed by hydraulic engineers in their study of water movement through confined spaces, such as in the soil. Probably the greatest single advance might be the development of some means for measuring negative pressures (tensions) in liquids, especially within a plant.

THE MOVEMENT OF ASSIMILATES

The main organic constituent that is moved in solution throughout the plant is sugar. Of course, amino acids also move within the plant, as do various hormones and even substances as complex as proteins and virus particles. We can begin our discussion of sugar translocation with the basic information that movement takes place in a direction from point of origin (source) to point of utilization (sink). The point of origin is usually a photosynthesizing cell, but it could also be a cell that is converting insoluble starch to soluble sugar. The point of utilization can be any cell that uses sugar in metabolic processes such as respiration. These nonphotosynthesizing cells occur in the roots, the cortex, the pith rays, the lateral and terminal meristems, the flowers, and the fruits.

Mechanisms of movement: cytoplasmic streaming. Two principal mechanisms have been proposed to account for movement of sugars throughout the plant. One approach has been to think in terms of diffusion, but this is a very slow process, and mechanisms must be postulated to account for the observed rates. The cytoplasmic-streaming hypothesis (Fig. 12-4) is an example of such a mechanism. Rates of movement are accounted for by cytoplasmic streaming, but diffusion plays a role in moving materials from one cell to its adjacent cell. We have already considered the process in discussing movement of dissolved substances through the symplast from the outer surfaces

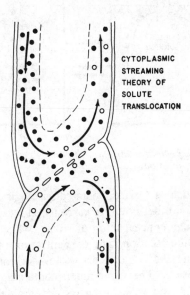

CYTOPLASMIC
STREAMING
THEORY OF
SOLUTE
TRANSLOCATION

Fig. 12-4. *The cytoplasmic-streaming theory of solute translocation, illustrated schematically. (From Frank B. Salisbury, "Translocation: The Movement of Dissolved Substances in Plants," in Jensen and Kavaljian,* Plant Biology Today: Advances and Challenges *(Belmont, Calif.: Wadsworth Publishing Co., Inc., 1963), by permission.*

of the root into the stele. In Fig. 12-4, the black dots represent one substance in high concentration and the white dots represent another substance in lower concentration, but moving in the opposite direction. Such a mechanism would permit movement in both directions, always from the source to the sink of the particular substance being translocated. It is an attractive mechanism, but it is untenable for mature sieve tubes, because in these elements the cytoplasm does not stream. Yet we can imagine that this mechanism may play a role in any instance where the cytoplasm does stream, such as in cortical cells, photosynthesizing cells in the leaf, and young sieve-tube elements.

Mechanisms of movement: pressure flow. The other approach suggests that assimilates move through the sieve-tube elements in a bulk flow of material. The mechanism that might create this mass flow is demonstrated by the model in Fig. 12-5, which was suggested in

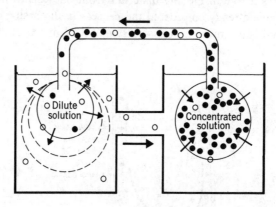

Fig. 12-5. *A schematic illustration of Münch's pressure-flow theory of solute translocation.*

1930 by E. Münch, a German plant physiologist. Two osmometers are connected by a tube. Both are surrounded by water. One osmometer contains a high concentration of solute, while the other contains a much more dilute solution. The concentration of substances in the water surrounding the osmometers is low in comparison with the concentration inside. The osmometer containing the concentrated solution takes up water by osmosis, developing a pressure. This pressure is transmitted to the other osmometer (with the speed of sound). In the second osmometer, where the concentration is low and the free energy relatively high, the pressure arriving from the first osmometer tends to increase the free energy until it is above that of the surrounding solution. Water then diffuses out of the second osmometer, resulting in a flow of material from the first osmometer to the second, and anything dissolved in this material is simply carried along in a bulk flow.

The pressure could also be relieved by expansion of the second osmometer, rather than by movement of material out of it. An example might be the growth of a fruit, and it is indicated by the broken lines in Fig. 12-5. The black dots indicate the main osmotic component, sugar, and the open circles represent another dissolved substance present at a much lower concentration. This second substance would simply move along with the first, and if it could pass through the membranes, it might even circulate throughout the system.

Figure 12-6 illustrates Münch's pressure-flow hypothesis as applied

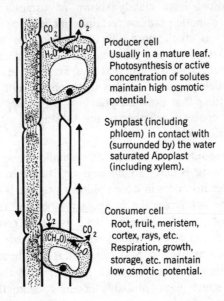

Fig. 12-6. *A schematic illustration of Münch's pressure-flow theory as applied to the plant.*

to the plant. The first osmometer is analogous to a producer cell in which osmotic potential is maintained high. The consumer cell where sugars are continuously being removed by respiration and other processes represents the second osmometer. The phloem elements (the symplast as a whole) represent the connecting link between the two osmometers, and the surrounding solution occurs in the apoplast. We should note that the plant system may never reach equilibrium, because sugars are continually being produced and used up, while Münch's physical model would reach equilibrium when enough material had been moved from the first osmometer to the second to make the concentrations equal in both.

How can we test Münch's mechanism in the plant? The following statement seems logical: *If* there is an osmotic gradient, *if* there is a pressure gradient, and *if* flow through sieve tubes (the symplast) can occur, *then* the pressure flow mechanism must exist in the plant. This is not to imply that the existence of such a mechanism would eliminate any other sort of mechanism.

The osmotic and pressure gradients. The presence of an osmotic gradient was indicated in Fig. 12-3. Furthermore, various workers have measured osmotic potentials at many points between leaves and roots. Often these measurements apply specifically to phloem sap. Such investigations have clearly shown an osmotic gradient. The presence of an osmotic gradient certainly implies a pressure gradient. Such a gradient is much more difficult to measure, however, and a gradient in pressures has not yet been conclusively demonstrated. Yet in the next paragraph we see that the material in the sieve-tube elements is under pressure, so we are probably not going too far astray in admitting that pressure gradients do occur. The remaining question, then, concerns whether or not substances will flow through the sieve-tube elements.

Bulk flow through sieve tubes. Many studies have been made in which phloem tissue is carefully cut and sap is seen to exude from it. Indeed, there are instances in which phloem exudate is of commercial importance. The palmyra palm in India may exude 11 liters of sap per day, and this sap may contain as high as 10 per cent sucrose with 0.25 per cent of dissolved mineral solutes. The flow in such cases may be as rapid as 100 to 500 centimeters per hour through the sieve tubes. This rate of flow, which is faster than the normal rate of flow in the intact plant, probably occurs because the pressure is relieved when the phloem elements are severed.

In recent years these studies have been greatly refined and extended by the use of phloem-"sucking" insects. Certain aphids insert their stylets directly and selectively into the sieve-tube elements of the phloem. Sap is then forced into their bodies by the pressure in the sieve-tube elements (they exert no active sucking processes themselves). Exudate even collects on the surface of their bodies where it is in turn consumed by ants. In recent studies, the aphid was allowed to insert the stylet into the phloem, and then the insect was cut off, leaving the stylet in place. Sap continued to exude through the cut stylet for a considerable period of time (days in some instances). In one instance in which rate of movement was about 100 centimeters per hour, it was calculated that the contents of 100 sieve-tube elements must be emptied each minute. Thus the entire contents of each sieve tube must move through the sieve plate in less than a second.

Lateral movement from sieve tubes has also been demonstrated (for example, by the use of radioactive tracers), although it is much more restricted than longitudinal movement. This restriction would be expected on the basis of the symplast concept. If there are consuming cells in the neighborhood of a sieve-tube element (such as phloem parenchyma, rays, cortex, or pith cells), then lateral movement through plasmodesmata would be a natural result of the phloem's function as a distribution system.

We have now met all of the conditions established above, and so we must conclude that a pressure-flow mechanism must operate within the plant.

The importance of pressure flow: mass movement. How important is such a mechanism in the over-all translocation of organic solutes? If natural and applied solutes move in the plant along with the sugar (the main osmotic component), we might feel that the mass-flow mechanism is, indeed, an important one. If, on the other hand, substances move strictly according to their own concentration gradients, as might be accounted for by cytoplasmic streaming, we would be tempted to conclude that pressure flow is important only under certain conditions.

A great deal of work extending over the last three decades seems to allow the conclusion that substances nearly always move in the same direction in the phloem. Early work in the 1930s involving the movement of plant viruses was extensive and impressive. More recently a considerable amount of work has involved the weed killer 2,4-D. Since this compound causes bending and other visible responses in the plant, it is easy to apply it to one site and subsequently know where it goes in the plant. Numerous workers since 1945 have shown that 2,4-D always follows the movement of sugar. If the leaf is darkened for a period of time, and 2,4-D is applied, it will not move out until the leaf has either been allowed to photosynthesize or been treated externally with sugar. Nor will 2,4-D move into a leaf that is exporting sugar.

Even more recently, this basic conclusion has been fortified by the use of many radioactive minerals and organic molecules, including various growth regulators, antibiotics, etc. In some cases it has been shown that such molecules will even move against their own concentration gradient, as long as they are moving with the sugar. In other experiments, radioactive (tritiated) water and labeled solutes have been shown to move together in the same direction. In some of these cases, any sort of accelerated diffusion mechanism, such as cytoplasmic streaming, simply does not account for the observed results. We may conclude, then, that since diverse substances follow a mass-flow pattern, the pressure-flow mechanism of Münch must be important in the plant.

Rates of phloem transport and mechanisms of movement. How do rates of movement agree with the pressure-flow mechanism (or any mechanism for that matter)? This is the remaining serious problem in understanding plant translocation. Rates are simply too fast to be accounted for by present theories. If we consider maximum rates of 150 centimeters per hour, and then take into account the fact that the sieve-plate openings make up only about one-eleventh of the over-all cross-sectional area of the sieve tube, we must conclude that substances move through these openings at the rate of 16.5 meters per hour. This seems like a phenomenal rate for openings that are so small. And in severed phloem elements, the rate may be even many times faster than this! Such extreme rates often do result in plugging of the sieve plates, probably by dislodging materials to produce so-called slime plugs.

Metabolism and phloem transport. In a number of studies, it has been shown that the sieve-tube elements are functional only when they are alive and metabolizing. If they are killed, or if respiration is inhibited in any way, movement through them ceases. Münch's model will not help in understanding this requirement for metabolism. What does it all mean? Obviously phloem cells are quite different from other plant cells. The nucleus is gone, the tonoplast is indistinct or missing, and there are usually companion cells present. Certain attempts to measure respiration rates have indicated that they are different when one compares phloem with other cells. What does this have to do with translocation?

The physiology of phloem cells must be studied, but this is very difficult because such study may easily disturb their function. Sieve tubes and plates must be carefully examined with the electron microscope. A. S. Crafts wonders if the surrounding cytoplasm in the sieve-plate pores somehow cause water to be in a superfluid condition (water molecules ordered in such a way that they flow with virtually no viscosity). Could we relate such a thing to metabolism? Accumulation of substances such as sugars into the sieve-tube elements has been demonstrated in some systems. "Activated diffusion" (related to metabolism) across the sieve plates has often been postulated, but so far we are left without convincing evidence.

Bidirectional movement. The report that bidirectional movement sometimes occurs in the phloem elements has caused consternation over the years. If it could be shown that one substance moves in one direction in a given phloem sieve tube while another substance is moving in the opposite direction, Münch's pressure-flow mechanism could not apply in that case. Actually this has never been rigorously demonstrated. Nevertheless, there is considerable evidence for bidirectional movement within a single vascular bundle.

Much of the older work utilized dyes, but recently O. Biddulph and R. Cory at Washington State University have approached the problem with considerable elegance using radioactive tracers. An upper leaf on a bean plant was exposed to labeled carbon dioxide, which was photosynthetically incorporated into radioactive sugar. Labeled phosphorus was applied as phosphate to the leaf immediately below. The position of the phosphorus could be determined on a radioautograph by shielding out the weak rays from the carbon. After many months, the phosphorus had decayed away, and the position of the carbon could then be determined. In a majority of trials, Biddulph and Cory found bidirectional movement of these two substances. In some cases, the bidirectional movement took place in separate bundles, and Münch's pressure-flow mechanism could always be used in explaining these cases. In other instances, however, bidirectional movement occurred in the same bundle, and within the limits of their ability to resolve the two substances, movement appeared to occur within the same phloem elements.

In the second instance, they were able to locate the bidirectional movement in young phloem tissue. This is exactly where we might expect such an occurrence, because cytoplasm is known to stream in these immature phloem elements. Their conclusion was that both mechanisms must operate in the bean plant. There is no reason why they should not, so we must not eliminate cytoplasmic-streaming mechanisms from our thinking just because we accept pressure-flow mechanisms. If the cytoplasm streams, and if diffusion will occur from cytoplasm to cytoplasm in adjacent cells, the mechanism must operate.

THE TRANSLOCATION OF DISSOLVED SUBSTANCES

As should be apparent by now, the field of translocation is a broad one, and while space limitations will not permit a detailed discussion, we shall devote a paragraph to each of six topics.

Variety in the way things move within the plant. Phosphorus, potassium, sodium, chlorine, sulfur, and some nitrogen compounds are quite mobile within the plant, while calcium, magnesium, iron, and cobalt seem to be bound in plant tissue so that they are essentially immobile after they arrive in the leaf via the transpiration stream. Work using various radioactively labeled weed killers and other growth regulators indicates that mobilities of these substances vary considerably from one compound to another. These different mobilities remind us of a chromatogram, in which compounds are separated from each other by their solubility in a solvent, and by the tenacity with which they adhere to some material such as filter paper. Some substances must be more soluble in the liquid of cytoplasm or sieve-tube elements, and some must be more tenaciously adsorbed by the protein and cell-wall materials of tissues.

Free circulation of substances in the plant. In sugar cane, radio-active phosphorus will move out of the treated leaf through the phloem system into the root, back into the apoplast, up through the xylem, into the leaf, and around again a number of times. Other compounds are also capable of circulation within the plant, but calcium, magnesium, and cobalt apparently will not circulate under any conditions. William Harvey's discovery of circulation in animals was followed by a search for an equivalent circulation in plants. Since there is no pumping organ comparable to the heart, it was concluded that such a circulation in plants did not occur. Now we discover that if individual substances are considered, circulation of a sort does take place.

Movement of gases through the plant's intercellular space system. Gases are reported to move from the upper parts of the plant down to the roots at rates as high as 50 meters per hour or even higher. This movement would occur through the gas-filled intercellular spaces of a plant (which may make up as much as 20 per cent by volume of a land plant and 70 per cent or more in the case of certain aquatic stems).

Alpha-methoxyphenylacetic acid secreted by roots. Workers at Beltsville, Maryland, found that when this compound was applied to the tops of various plants, it could be collected subsequently in the nutrient medium around the roots. It could then be absorbed by neighboring plants with intermingling root systems. Secretion from the roots depended on metabolic activity and was not simply a leakage through the apoplast system. The finding might have considerable application in agriculture, if it could be applied to specific compounds such as those that might be capable of controlling pathogens in the soil. It would be necessary only to spray the chemical on the mature crop and expect it to end up finely distributed in the soil. The finding is also of ecological importance, because substances that are secreted by one plant may be inhibitory to the growth of another.

Polar transport. The polar transport of auxin was discussed in Chapter 8. It has also been reported that sugars will move only in a polar direction out of a leaf. Such polar movement is presently a complete mystery. The implication is that the cell is distinctly different from one end to another, and that this difference will result in very specific functional phenomena such as control in direction of move-

Fig. 12-7. *Translocation of the excitation stimulus in* Mimosa pudica. *From Frank B. Salisbury, in* Plant Biology Today *(Belmont, Calif.: Wadsworth Publishing Co., Inc., 1963), by permission.*

ment. The whole finding seems to imply aspects of the translocation problem which have scarcely been discussed or even considered.

Movement of the excitation stimulus in mimosa. *Mimosa,* the sensitive plant, folds up its leaflets and its leaves upon contact. If one touches the plant with some object, the whole plant is likely to be disturbed, and all its leaves and leaflets will fold up almost at once. If, however, one is extremely careful to contact only a portion of the plant (one way is by using a flame as in Fig. 12-7), then the folding progresses from the point of contact back through the plant body. There is no nervous system in plants, and this response comes about because a chemical stimulus is translocated from the point of contact. The series of photographs in Fig. 12-7 demonstrate the phenomenon and indicate that some activities of higher plants are easily noticeable. Eleven seconds after the stimulation by the flame, most of the leaflets had folded up on the one branch that was contacted. Eleven seconds later, the stimulus had moved into other branches, and by the end of the 60-second interval, all of the plant within the area of the photograph had responded.

13

THE FLOWER

In higher plants, as in higher animals, the cells that are destined to play an active part in sexual reproduction—the germ plasm of the organism—are found associated with structures and tissues specialized to aid in this extremely important activity. The germ plasm of some of the gymnosperms (naked-seeded plants), such as pine, hemlock, and spruce, makes up a small part of the specialized reproductive structures called cones. In the angiosperms (covered-seeded plants), the sex cells are intimately associated with the flower. The *flower* is an assemblage of parts consisting of an axis and a number of lateral appendages concerned primarily with sexual reproduction. Put another way, a flower is a shoot system made up of a stem, sterile leaves, and fertile leaves (assuming that all parts are present).

FLORAL MORPHOLOGY

The stem or axis of an individual flower is referred to as the *pedicel* if the plant bears several or many flowers in groups or clusters. If the plant bears individual flowers, the flowering stem or stalk is called a *peduncle.* (This term is also used to refer to a major floral axis, to which many pedicels and hence many flowers are attached.)

A typical flower is made up of four different kinds of leaf-like appendages—the *sepals,* the *petals,* the *stamens,* and the *carpels* (Fig. 13-1).

The sepals are usually green and resemble foliage (leaves) more closely than the other parts of the flower. All of the sepals together make up the *calyx.*

The *petals* most often are brightly colored and are the most conspicuous parts of the flower. Collectively, the petals make up the *corolla.* The calyx and corolla together make up the *perianth,* or the nonessential parts of the flower. These floral parts are nonessential in the sense that, because they contain no germ plasm, they play no *direct* role in sexual reproduction.

The *stamens* are the organs that produce spores, which in turn ultimately produce the male gametes. They consist of two parts: a

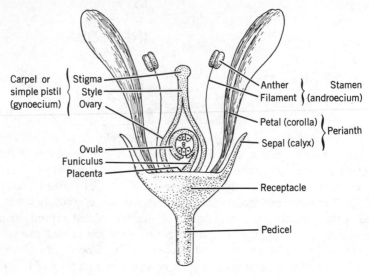

Fig. 13-1. *Generalized diagram of a flower.*

long, basal, sterile *filament,* which bears a terminal fertile structure, the *anther.* The germ plasm that eventually gives rise to the male gametes or sperm cells is contained within the anther. The stamens make up the *androecium,* collectively.

The *carpels* are organs that also produce spores, which in turn ultimately lead to the formation of female gametes. The carpels consist of three parts: a terminal *stigma,* an elongated *style,* and a fertile, basal *ovary.* The germ plasm that will eventually produce the female gametes or eggs is contained within the ovary. The carpels collectively constitute the *gynoecium.* If the gynoecium consists of a single carpel, the term *simple pistil* may be used to designate this floral part. If the gynoecium is made up of several united carpels, the structure may be referred to as a *compound pistil.* A gynoecium made up of many free carpels may also be designated as one consisting of many simple pistils.

The gynoecium and the androecium are the essential parts of the flower, since the tissue that will ultimately produce the gametes makes up a part of these floral structures. Since positive identification and classification of a given species of angiosperm is based in large part on the morphology of the flower, a complex terminology has been formulated over the years in order to describe adequately the almost endless variation in floral structure present in nature. Some of the basic concepts concerning floral morphology will now be considered.

Flowers in which all four parts (calyx, corolla, androecium, and gynoecium) are present are *complete* flowers. If one or more part is missing, the flower is *incomplete*. Flowers with both essential parts present (androecium and gynoecium), regardless of the presence or absence of the perianth parts, are *perfect*. Flowers with either the stamens or the carpels missing are *imperfect*. Plants that have imperfect flowers may be either *monoecious* or *dioecious*. Monoecious plants have both staminate and carpelate flowers on the same plant body but in different positions. Dioecious plants have only staminate or only carpelate flowers on a given plant body. Flowers that are imperfect are always incomplete, but incomplete flowers are not necessarily imperfect.

The specialized end of the pedicel or peduncle to which the flower parts are attached is termed the *receptacle*. If the receptacle is cone-shaped or convex, the sepals, because of their position on the outside of the flower, are attached to the outer edge or rim. The carpels, since they make up the innermost group of parts, are attached to the center or summit of the receptacle. Such a flower is *hypogynous* (below the gynoecium—see Fig. 13-2a) because the stamens, petals,

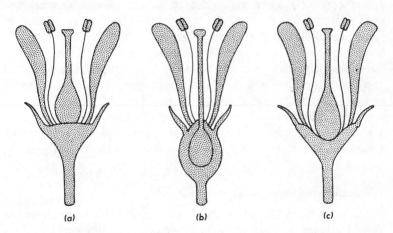

Fig. 13-2. *Diagrams of (a) hypogynous, (b) epigynous, and (c) perigynous flowers.*

and sepals are all attached at locations lower down on the receptacle than the carpels. A hypogynous flower has a superior ovary, since the ovary is positioned above the rest of the floral appendages. If the receptacle is deeply concave, the gynoecium is situated in the bottom of the concavity, whereas the androecium, corolla, and calyx are located above the gynoecium. Such a flower is *epigynous* (above the gynoecium—Fig. 13-2b) and has an inferior ovary, since the ovary is positioned below the rest of the floral parts. An intermediate condition exists when the receptacle is essentially flat or shallowly concave. In such cases the sepals, petals, and stamens are positioned around the carpels (attached to the receptacle neither conspicuously above nor below the carpels) and the flower is *perigynous* (around the gynoecium—Fig. 13-2c). Often in such cases, the ovary is half-superior or half-inferior.

Floral parts are often united in various ways. Union of like or similar parts (sepal united to sepal, petal united to petal, etc.) is known as *coalescence*. Union of unlike parts (petals united to sepals, stamens united to petals, etc.) is termed *adnation*. A common type of adnation is the union of the stamen filaments to the petals.

Regular flowers are those that exhibit radial symmetry. Irregular flowers exhibit dorsiventral symmetry.

SEXUAL REPRODUCTION

The life cycles of higher plants differ in general from those of higher animals in that plant life cycles may be separated into two different phases, based on a change in the relative chromosome number from *diploid* in one phase to *haploid* in the other phase. In plants, the diploid phase produces haploid spores that give rise to a haploid organism that produces *gametes*. Union of gametes restores the diploid condition and results in the formation of a new diploid organism. In higher animals, the diploid organism gives rise directly to haploid gametes that unite and restore the diploid condition. No separate haploid phase is present. In higher plants, the conspicuous, evident organism is the diploid (sporophyte) plant. The haploid (gametophyte) plant is very small and is often evident only to the trained observer.

Microspore and Microgametophyte Development

The cells within the anther that constitute the male germ plasm are termed *microsporocytes* or *pollen mother cells,* and occur in four discrete groups. Each group, along with some associated accessory tissue, makes up a *pollen sac*. Hence each anther contains four pollen sacs. The pollen mother cells are diploid. Each pollen mother cell divides *meiotically,* forming four haploid *microspores*. The haploid nucleus of each microspore divides mitotically, producing two haploid nuclei (Fig. 13-3). The binucleate microspore, after undergoing some significant changes in shape and wall morphology, becomes a *pollen grain*. The pollen grain is the male haploid plant (*microgametophyte*).

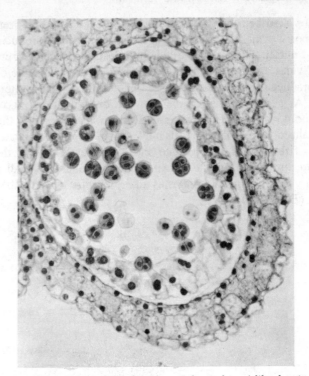

Fig. 13-3. *Cross section through a part of the anther of lily showing various stages of microsporogenesis.* × *450.*

With further maturation, the anther splits open, releasing the pollen grains, after which they are carried by the wind or by insects to the stigma of the same or of different flowers. The transfer of pollen from the anther to the stigma is called *pollination.*

Megaspore and Megagametophyte Development

While the pollen grains are developing in the pollen sacs of the stamens, a somewhat similar sequence of events occurs in the ovary of the carpel. The cells that constitute the female germ plasm are called *megasporocytes* or *megaspore mother cells* and occur as single cells localized in special structures or *ovules* contained within the ovary. A given ovary may contain a single ovule, or more frequently, contains several to many ovules. Each ovule consists of a small, somewhat spherical body containing a single megaspore mother cell. The ovule is attached to the ovary at the *placenta* by means of a stalk, the *funiculus.*

The megasporocyte of a given ovule undergoes *meiosis,* producing four haploid megaspores. Three of the four megaspores degenerate and are resorbed by the surrounding tissue. The one remaining megaspore, which is haploid, undergoes mitosis, producing two haploid nuclei. These nuclei divide mitotically, producing four nuclei; each divides again, resulting in the formation of eight haploid nuclei, all contained within a single large cell located in the center of the ovule. At about the same time that the divisions take place in the megaspore and its derivative nuclei, the *integuments* of the ovule (specialized layers of tissue, usually two in number, located on the flanks of the ovule) differentiate and overarch the end of the ovule opposite the region of attachment of the funiculus. A small pore or opening, the *micropyle,* remains as a port of entry between the integuments (Fig. 13-4).

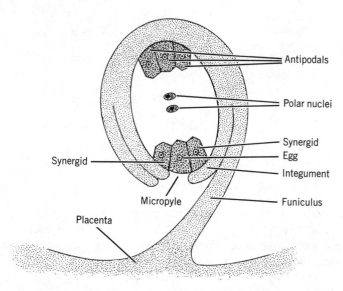

Fig. 13-4. *Diagrammatic vertical cross section through an ovule containing the mature megagametophyte.*

The eight nuclei that are derived mitotically from the single surviving megaspore now become oriented within the large central cell of the ovule in the following manner: three migrate to the end opposite the micropyle, three migrate to the micropylar end, and two remain in or near the center. Thin cell walls, or in some cases membranes, are formed, resulting in the formation of an eight-nucleate, seven-celled structure, the *embryo sac.* The embryo sac is the female haploid plant or *megagametophyte.* (The large central cell contains *two* haploid nuclei.) Together with the pollen grain, the embryo sac represents the haploid phase of the life cycle. Of the seven cells making up the embryo sac, the three furthest from the micropyle are the *antipodals*. Two of the three cells at the end nearest to the micropyle are the *synergids*. The third cell in this group is the female gamete or egg. All three of these cells are in close contact. The large central cell between the antipodals and the egg apparatus (egg plus the two synergids) contains the two *polar nuclei*.

The type of embryo-sac development just described is encountered very commonly in diverse groups of angiosperms. Another type, less common but, unfortunately, most often used in general botany laboratories is exemplified by *Lilium*. In the development of the *Lilium* embryo sac, meiosis occurs in the megasporocyte, producing four megaspores, all of which remain functional. The four haploid megaspores then divide mitotically in the following manner: one megaspore divides, producing two haploid nuclei; the other three megaspores give rise to a single mitotic spindle and divide, producing two *triploid nuclei*. After migration of the nuclei and formation of cell walls or membranes, the mature *Lilium* embryo sac is a seven-celled, eight-nucleate structure consisting of three triploid antipodals, a large central cell containing one triploid and one haploid polar nucleus, two haploid synergids, and a haploid egg.

After a pollen grain is transferred to a stigma, it germinates, producing a *pollen tube*. One of the two nuclei of the pollen grain, the *tube nucleus,* migrates into the tip of the rapidly penetrating pollen tube. The second or *generative nucleus* may also pass into the tube and take up a position some distance behind the tube nucleus. The pollen tube grows through the stylar tissue and into the ovary, and makes contact with the embryo sac by way of the micropyle.

Prior to or during pollen tube development, the generative nucleus divides mitotically, producing two *sperm nuclei*. The pollen tube enters the embryo sac, after which the end of the tube usually disintegrates, releasing the sperm nuclei. Soon afterwards, one sperm nucleus unites with the egg, forming a diploid *zygote*. The second sperm nucleus unites with the two polar nuclei, forming a triploid *primary endosperm cell*. (In the case of an embryo sac of the *Lilium* type, the primary endosperm cell would be pentaploid.) Union of sperm and egg is known as *fertilization* or *syngamy*. Union of the two polar nuclei and a sperm is known as *triple fusion*. Triple fusion and fertilization constitute a situation known as *double fertilization,* a constant characteristic of sexual reproduction in flowering plants.

The tube nucleus of the male gametophyte and the antipodals and synergids of the female gametophyte seem to play no direct role in double fertilization and usually disintegrate soon after the formation of the zygote and the primary endosperm cell.

With further development, the zygote becomes the embryo of the seed. The primary endosperm cell gives rise to the food-storage tissue of the seed, and the integuments produce the inner and outer seed coats. Hence the ovule matures into the seed. Concurrently with the development of the ovule into the seed, the ovary, containing the developing seed, matures into the fruit of the plant.

14

PHOTOBIOLOGY

Of the many environmental factors that influence plant and animal life, light may be the most interesting. There is something especially intriguing about the thought of plant growth being controlled by rays that travel 186,000 miles per second from a luminous body 93,000,000 miles away.

LIGHT

To understand how light acts on living organisms, one must first understand something about the nature of light, and so progress in this new and fascinating field of biology depends almost completely on findings in the science of physics. Light may vary in intensity, in duration (intensity may also change as a function of time), and in quality. Our understanding of light quality, however, is complicated at present by the fact that the physicist has two theories to explain light; and although the two theories are extremely difficult to reconcile, both have applications in our understanding of photobiology.

Light may first be described in terms of its wave nature, the various colors being a function of the wavelength of light (see Figs. 14-1 and 14-2). Blue light has wavelengths from about 400 to 500 millimicrons, green from about 500 to 560, and red from about 645 to 720 or longer. Of course blue-green, yellow, and orange fall at the borderlines between these colors. While waves are thought of as being propagated through some sort of medium, no medium is known in space which would transmit such waves (the ether was postulated to meet this need, but present physical theory has eliminated it). Nevertheless, many light phenomena, such as diffraction, can be understood only in relation to the wave nature of light.

On the other hand, the action of light is often best understood on the basis of its particulate nature. Light energy occurs in small, indivisible packets called *photons* or *quanta*. The energy of a quantum in the blue end of the spectrum may be nearly twice as great as the energy of a quantum in the red end. Certain phenomena, including photosynthesis, can be explained only through the quantum concept.

At any rate we know that, in nature, light varies in almost every way imaginable. Rotation of the earth results in changes in light intensity, duration, and quality (although the effect upon quality is probably least noticeable). Latitude, elevation, air polutents, water depth, clouds, shading, and many other factors also influence light intensity, duration, and quality. Indeed, the habits of animals, and to a far lesser extent the habits of plants, also influence the light absorbed by a given organism.

LIGHT ACTION

A fundamental principle in photobiology (or in any consideration of light action) is that *if light is to be effective it must be absorbed.* This absorbed light energy increases the energy of the ion, atom, or molecule that absorbs it, by various mechanisms such as raising an electron to a higher energy level. In most cases, the excited particle soon returns to the so-called ground state. If an electron has been raised, for example, it will fall back to its former level. The energy that must be released when the particle returns to the ground state may simply be converted to the over-all kinetic energy of the particle. That is, it is converted to heat. In certain instances, however, the energy is converted back to light, and this process is known as *fluorescence* (or *phosphorescence,* if the time interval between absorption and emission exceeds a small fraction of a second). As a general rule, the wavelength of fluorescent light is always somewhat longer (less energy per quantum) than the wavelength of the light that excited the absorbing particle. In a few instances that are of primary importance to our discussion of photobiology, the absorbed light energy may be converted to chemical bond energy as the particle returns to the ground state. Our most familiar example is that of *photosynthesis,* in which the absorbed light energy is finally converted to the chemical bond energy of carbohydrates and other compounds. This energy may subsequently be released by respiration or even by burning.

PHOTOBIOLOGICAL PROCESSES IN PLANTS

In higher plants, most photobiological responses fall into one of three broad groups.

Responses of Chlorophyll or Its Chemical Relatives

Photosynthesis might well be the most important photobiological response in both the plant and the animal kingdoms, since our entire energy supply depends upon it. In many angiosperms, the synthesis of chlorophyll also depends on light. A compound known as protochlorophyll is converted to chlorophyll by the action of light. Thus angiosperms that germinate in the dark appear colorless or only slightly greenish yellow when they are first brought out into the light, but after a few hours they become green. A pine seedling germinated in the dark, however, is green when it is first brought into the light.

Responses to Blue Light

In Chapter 8 we discussed the phenomenon of phototropism, in which stems grow toward the light. As noted, this is a response to blue light. Indeed, this response serves as an introduction to one of the most fundamental research tools in the field of photobiology. An investigator usually wants to obtain a so-called action spectrum in the early part of his investigation on light responses. In the case of phototropism, one might do this by exposing stems to equal intensities of light at various wavelengths or colors (see Fig. 8-4, p. 71). The amount of bending in response to this treatment is plotted as a function of the wavelength, as in Fig. 14-1. The next logical step is to find a pigment within the plant that absorbs light in a manner exactly comparable to the action spectrum, since light must be absorbed if it is to be effective. We measure the absorption spectrum of a suspected pigment by measuring the amount of light absorbed by the pigment at a given wavelength. Absorption spectra obtained in this way for the pigments beta-carotene and riboflavin are also shown in Fig. 14-1. If the absorption spectrum matches the action spectrum quite closely, then the investigator has evidence that the suspected pigment is indeed the one that absorbs the light, causing the photobiological response. For example, the absorption spectrum of chlorophyll very closely matches the action spectrum for photosynthesis.

As can be seen in Fig. 14-1, the absorption spectra of both beta-carotene and riboflavin match rather closely the action spectrum for phototropism. Since one pigment matches well in the blue part of the spectrum and the other somewhat better in the ultraviolet part of the spectrum, we cannot say definitely which of these two suspected pigments is responsible for the phototropic response. Most researchers feel that one of these two is the effective one, however, and it is possible that both of them contribute to the process.

Certain other responses, such as protoplasmic viscosity and photoreactivation of cells or tissues damaged by ultraviolet light, are also sensitive to blue light. The light-absorbing pigments have not been identified in these processes. A few other responses, such as the germination of certain seeds (various mustards, for example) and

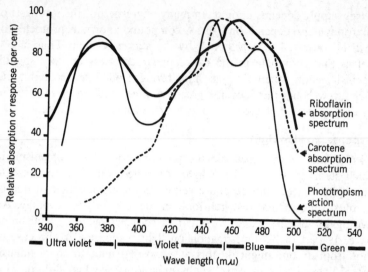

Fig. 14-1. *The action spectrum for phototropism and the absorption spectra of riboflavin and carotene. Note that the absorption spectrum of carotene matches the action spectrum quite well in the visible (slight shifting of the peaks often occurs upon extraction with special solvents), but fails to account for the peak in the ultraviolet—a peak nicely accounted for by riboflavin, which has only a poor match of peaks in the visible.*

the flowering of certain plants, are also sensitive to blue light and may be placed in this same general category, but it would be very simple to establish another category for them.

Responses Controlled by the Photomorphogenetic Pigment System: Phytochrome

There are a number of plant-growth responses that exhibit the same action spectrum. This action spectrum is especially remarkable because it displays a unique property of reversibility. Orange-red light between 620 and 670 millimicrons (with a peak at about 665 millimicrons) causes a given effect, while far-red light from 710 to 750 millimicrons (peak at about 730 millimicrons) will nullify or reverse the effect. Fig. 14-2 shows a standard action spectrum for these responses. The pigment that is effective in activating these phenomena has been termed *phytochrome*.

This field is an active area of research today. It is especially intriguing to realize that many varied responses might all be controlled by the same fundamental biochemical system. Furthermore, the pigment that controls these responses has recently been studied in plant extracts, and much active research is being devoted to purification and further

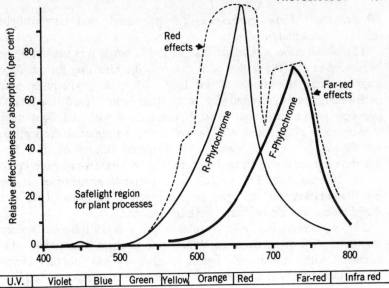

Fig. 14-2. *Relative spectra for phytochrome and its effects. The broken lines show generalized action spectra, indicating that the action spectra for various processes may be expected to fall within the curves shown, although none may match them exactly (shifting of peaks caused by chlorophyll screening, etc., may account for the variability). The solid lines indicate measured absorption spectra for the two forms of phytochrome. As such they may be thought of as idealized action spectra. Reprinted with permission from Frank B. Salisbury,* The Flowering Process, *1963, Pergamon Press Limited.*

study of this phytochrome system. We will outline the various responses and discuss each of them very briefly.

Germination of certain seeds. The red–far-red system was initially observed in the germination of the Grand Rapids variety of lettuce. A powerful spectroscope had been built at the United States Department of Agriculture Plant Industry Laboratories at Beltsville, Maryland. The light source was a powerful carbon arc lamp, making it possible to get relatively high intensities even after the beam of light had been broken into its component colors by passing it through a prism. It was known that the Grand Rapids variety of lettuce seeds required light for germination. They were moistened and then placed along the projected spectrum. Seeds in the blue and green part of the spectrum germinated only about 20 per cent, at the level typical of seeds germinated in the dark. Seeds in the orange-red part of the spectrum, however, germinated nearly 100 per cent. Samples of seeds in the far-red part of the spectrum germinated significantly less than

20 per cent. Thus orange-red light promoted, and far-red light inhibited, germination.

The observation was made first in 1937, but it was not until the beginning of the 1950s that someone had the idea that far-red light might reverse the effects of red light. When this experiment was performed, such a reversal did occur. Red light caused nearly 100 per cent germination, but if seeds illuminated with red light were subsequently illuminated with far-red light, germination dropped to less than 20 per cent. If, however, seeds treated with red and then far-red were subsequently treated with red, germination went back up to nearly 100 per cent. This process was reversible many times. If the last illumination was red light, germination was high, and if the last illumination was far-red light, germination was low.

The workers at Beltsville postulated that a single pigment system was in control of germination. When this pigment system was illuminated with orange-red light, it shifted into another form (F-phytochrome), as illustrated by the following equation:

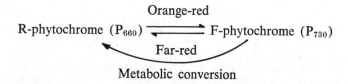

Orange-red

R-phytochrome (P_{660}) $\rightleftharpoons$ F-phytochrome (P_{730})

Far-red

Metabolic conversion

The F-phytochrome absorbed far-red light, which converted it back to R-phytochrome. Various lines of reasoning based on these and other experiments indicated that the F-phytochrome was converted metabolically within the plant back to the R-phytochrome condition, even in darkness, but this process was not instantaneous and required a certain time interval—many hours in the case of the lettuce seeds. If F-phytochrome were essential for the germination process to proceed, then the scheme above would explain the experimental results.

Since these initial studies, much more has been discovered about the germination response to red light. Many details relating to times and temperatures of the various treatments have been worked out, and a number of other seeds that also germinate in response to F-phytochrome have been discovered. Indeed, certain spores of ferns and mosses also appear to germinate in response to F-phytochrome.

Formation of certain plant pigments. Other phytochrome-controlled responses were studied at Beltsville. One of these is the synthesis of certain *anthocyanins* (water-soluble pigments that are usually brightly colored—often blue, orange, or red) in the skins of apples and turnips and in the organs of various other plants. *Carotenoids* (fat-soluble pigments, also brightly colored—usually orange, yellow, or red) are also synthesized in the skin of tomato fruits in response to red light. In any of these systems, small samples of the plant tissue such as the skin of the apple can be floated on solutions of sugars and other compounds in petri dishes. Such a simple system is easy to illuminate, and tissue can be ground up and studied biochemically in an attempt to understand the mechanisms of the light response. We now know more about the biochemistry of phytochrome action as it controls synthesis of anthocyanin or carotenoid pigments than we do about its action in any other instance.

Elongation of internodes. Many plant stems elongate very strikingly in response to far-red illumination, and this elongation is inhibited by red illumination. Again the action spectra implicate the phytochrome system. In some instances, the actual amount of elongation depends on the balance between the red and the far-red light used to illuminate the plants for a relatively short period just before they are placed in the dark. Attempts are being made to relate this response to the action of auxins and gibberellins (see Chapter 8).

Unbending of the epicotyl hook in bean and other plants. When a bean seedling germinates, the tip of the stem is bent around to form a hook. As this hook emerges from the soil, it straightens in response to red light (the phytochrome system). The angle of curvature can be accurately measured, and so it is possible to carry out detailed quantitative studies with this system.

The expansion of leaves. In plants that are grown in the dark, not only is there a tendency toward stem elongation, but the leaves are usually greatly reduced in size. This syndrome of elongated stems and unexpanded leaves is called *etiolation*. Just as stem elongation is inhibited by red light (F-phytochrome), so leaf expansion is promoted.

In the laboratory, small discs are cut from unexpanded leaves and floated on various solutions. They may then be illuminated and treated with chemicals, and their subsequent expansion may be accurately measured. Not only is leaf expansion promoted by red light and reversed by far-red light, but it is also promoted by sugars and kinetin or its relatives and by cobaltous ion. The significance of these findings is not yet apparent.

Flowering in response to day length. In Chapter 15, phytochrome is discussed in detail in relation to the flowering process.

Induction and breaking of dormancy. In temperate regions, many plants become dormant (drop their leaves, etc.) in response to the shortening day length. Some plants come out of dormancy in the spring in response to lengthening days. This appears to be another example of control by the phytochrome system.

Establishing circadian rhythms. We shall see in the next chapter that plant measurement of time, as displayed in periodical leaf movements, is often influenced strongly by light. Although much more work needs to be done, there is reason to believe that this response is also mediated through the phytochrome system.

Miscellaneous responses. Limited information indicates that the phytochrome system may be involved in *epinasty* (twisting and bending of stems under certain conditions), leaf abscission, bulb formation (such as in onions), production of rhizomes, succulency of leaf tissue, expression of sex, development of roots, formation of plastids within the cell, regeneration of protochlorophyll (a precursor to chlorophyll), chromosome breakage due to X rays, root formation, and some other processes as well.

It is important to note that the red–far-red system (presumably phytochrome) has been demonstrated in the green algae, the Bryophytes, the ferns, and both gymnosperms and angiosperms. It does not appear (as yet) in the fungi or the other groups of algae.

EXTRACTION OF PHYTOCHROME

What is perhaps one of the most outstanding recent scientific achievements in the field of plant physiology occurred in June of 1959, when the phytochrome system was first demonstrated in a plant extract. Early work with the germination of lettuce seeds and other systems had established a solid foundation of understanding about the nature of this pigment system. Its ability to absorb light had been calculated from experiments with seeds or whole plants. The concentration of the pigment in the plant tissue could be estimated accurately from such experiments. The *kinetics* (time course) of conversion of F-phytochrome to R-phytochrome had been studied. Other details of action of the pigment were also either fairly well known or at least suspected, but all attempts to apply the usual methods of biochemical study to this system had failed, partially because it was present in such small amounts. It was known that the pigment could be recognized by its color (its absorption spectrum), and most important, by its ability to be converted from one color to another by irradiation with far-red or red light.

Isolation of phytochrome became feasible with the development of a sensitive instrument that could detect very slight color changes in extremely dense samples. (For example, the absorption spectrum of an ordinary 2-inch piece of wood could be determined.) It was necessary to determine the difference in absorption of a sample (whole plants or an extract) at 665 millimicrons and at 735 millimicrons. Of course, illumination at 665 millimicrons would convert the pigment to the form that absorbed light at 735 millimicrons, so it was necessary to determine the absorption with extreme rapidity and with a relatively small amount of light. The pigment was initially converted to one form or another by illumination with high intensities of red or far-red light, and then the difference in absorption between the two peaks was determined 16 times per second by a special modification of the instrument.

Using this means, workers first demonstrated the pigment in intact corn seedlings, which proved to be a rich source of the material. The seedlings could then be ground up and extracted in various ways, and a search for the pigment could be carried out in the various fractions of the extract.

Phytochrome proved to be a protein, although it has not yet been possible to obtain it in a completely pure condition. It has been concentrated, however, to the point where its color becomes apparent to the human eye. Indeed, the pigment, when centrifuged into a pellet at the bottom of a test tube, can be seen to change color when it is illuminated with red or far-red light. There are many problems for future investigations, including the complete purification of the pigment, characterization of the part of the molecule responsible for light absorption, and detailed biochemical investigations of its mode of action in plant tissues. At present it seems apparent that the F-phytochrome form is the one that is biologically active, but there is a great deal to learn about how it acts. It is present in such extremely low concentrations in plant tissue that its ability to control growth responses is most impressive. Responses to something like 40 to 100 molecules per cell have been observed, although 10,000 times this much may be required for full response.

OTHER PIGMENT SYSTEMS

In addition to the plant responses to light mentioned above, we have reason to believe that other important light-sensitive systems may exist in the plant. Certain plant-growth phenomena (such as the opening of the hook at the top of a lettuce seedling) will occur in response to relatively high intensities of blue or far-red light applied for a fairly long time. There are no signs of any sort of reversibility. It may be possible to understand these results on the basis of phytochrome, but it is also very likely that a separate pigment system is operating in these instances.

Most phytochrome-controlled responses require only very small amounts of light (sometimes at intensities below those to which the human eye is sensitive). Yet, in nature, plants are exposed to much higher intensities. Hence any study of plant-growth responses to these higher light energies will contribute to an area of our understanding that is presently being rather neglected.

15

BIOLOGICAL TIME

MEASUREMENT

Man is clearly able to sense time, sometimes quite accurately. For example, most of us are able to wake up at the same time of day with a little practice. One wonders whether plants and animals also have the ability to measure time. Regular patterns of migration, flowering, etc., might lead one to suspect that this is the case (day length might be measured to detect season), but on the other hand, occurrences that take place at a given time of year might be responses to changes in temperature or other climatic conditions.

THE BIOLOGICAL CLOCK

Occasional scientific papers before and during the nineteenth century mention in one way or another biological time measurement. A persistent rhythm in any plant or animal function, which continues even when the organism is placed in unchanging environmental conditions, would indicate an ability to measure time. Many rhythms were observed in the nineteenth century, but seldom was there any clear-cut demonstration that these rhythms were not caused by rhythms in the external environment. In 1920, two workers at the Plant Industry Station at Beltsville, Maryland, discovered that certain plants flower in response to the length of day and night. These workers, W. W. Garner and H. A. Allard, termed the phenomenon *photoperiodism*, indicating that a response to the *length* of day and night quite clearly indicates an ability of the organism to measure time. If we can assign a date to the discovery of biological timing, it probably should be 1920, the year of publication of the article by Garner and Allard.

In 1929, I. Beling discovered that honey bees could be trained to feed at certain times of the day, and this quite clearly indicated a biological time measurement (a time memory). By the 1950s there was an active area of research relating to this problem, involving many scientists. The term *biological clock* then entered the literature.

Perhaps the most striking recent discovery is that certain birds are able to navigate by the position of the moon or the sun (and perhaps even the stars). Since these change throughout the day and throughout the season, a very accurate time-measuring ability is clearly implied.

Persistent rhythms. In the late 1920s, Dr. Erwin Bünning, now at the University of Tübingen, began to study intensively the daily movements of leaves. Leaves of the common bean plant change from a relatively horizontal daytime position to a nearly vertical nighttime position. Bünning showed that this phenomenon continues to occur even when the plants are placed in continuous darkness at constant temperature. Often the movements persist for a number of days, usually about a week. This seems to indicate that the timing mechanism that controls the rhythmicity of movement is not itself a response to daily changes in light and temperature, but that it might well be located within the plant. Since these pioneering studies of Bünning, many facets of the problem have been studied in detail, and many other instances of persistent rhythms have been observed, such as flower opening and closing, the growth rate of certain seedlings, root pressures, the activities of several enzymes, and discharge of spores in certain fungi. The respiration rate of certain tissues seems to follow a persistent rhythm, as does mitosis and volume of the nucleus in some plants. A most interesting and intensively studied system is a marine green algae that emits light with peaks of intensity separated by about 24 hours. Persistent rhythms are also easily observed in many animals.

Photoperiodism. This kind of biological time measurement, originally discovered by Garner and Allard, also appears to be widespread in the plant and animal kingdom. Flowering in response to long and short days is a good example, and many plants become dormant or break dormancy in response to the relative length of day and night. The germination of certain seeds is influenced by day length, although this is not nearly so common as the more direct response to light described in the last chapter. Vegetative growth is commonly strongly influenced by length of day or night.

Thermoperiodism. Many plants respond to cycles of alternating temperature. Growth is best when nights are cooler than days, although in a very few plants the reverse is true. It is not completely clear whether this is an example of a persistent rhythm of sensitivity to temperature or a separate phenomenon in itself. Actually, responses to day length can be interpreted as persistent rhythms of sensitivity to light.

SOME CHARACTERISTICS OF CIRCADIAN RHYTHMS

Accuracy of the clocks. Persistent rhythms having a period of about 24 hours are called circadian (circa = approximately; diem = day). The rhythms mentioned above may have periods that match the days, the cycles of the moon, the tides, or even in some cases (notably seed germination) the year. As a rule, these cycles are seldom highly accurate. In the case of circadian or daily rhythms, the peaks of function (such as leaf movement) may vary from about 22 to 28 hours. The average for a number of members within a population frequently approximates 24 hours, but any given individual is quite likely to run either slow or fast (Fig. 15-1).

Normally, organisms are entrained to a 24-hour rhythm by the daily cycle of light and darkness. Experimentally they can be entrained to cycles that vary by quite a bit from 24 hours, but there is always a limit to how much these cycles can differ from the "normal" one.

Setting the clocks. In the case of leaf movement and other persistent rhythms, the manifestation may be initially timed by some environmental stimulus, usually an exposure to light. A population of bean plants, for example, grown under continuous conditions from the time of germination, shows either a random leaf movement or none at all. If the plants are then placed in darkness for a time and subsequently exposed to perhaps an hour of sunlight before being returned to constant dark conditions, the leaf movements of all the plants become synchronized, beginning at the exposure to light following darkness. In some instances (for example, the cocklebur), transfer from light to darkness initiates and synchronizes the rhythms. A sharp temperature change may also evoke the rhythm. In nature, these clock-setting mechanisms keep the cycles entrained with the natural daily cycle.

In the case of rhythms caused by exposure to light, existing evidence seems to implicate the phytochrome system, but the problem requires further study.

Sensitivity to temperature. Probably the most remarkable aspect of biological time measurement, in addition to the existence of the phenomenon itself, is that it is in many cases only slightly influenced by temperature. Leaf-movement cycles in plants are frequently lengthened somewhat by lower temperatures and shortened by higher temperatures, but the temperature effect is much less even in these cases than one might expect. A temperature change of 10°C commonly influences the leaf-movement cycle only by a factor of 1.2.

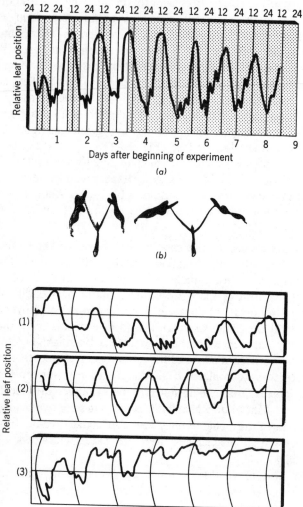

Fig. 15-1. *Diurnal leaf movements. Fig. (a) shows that leaf movements continue after plants are placed in continuous darkness; (b) indicates the relative positions of bean seedling leaves at night (left) and during daytime (right); on the graphs, the highest points indicate the night position (maximum lowering of the leaves); (c) shows bean leaf movements (1) in continuous darkness, (2) in continuous red light, and (3) in continuous far-red light; the rhythm becomes extinguished in far-red light but not in red light. From Erwin Bünning,* The Physiological Clock *(Springer-Verlag, 1964), by permission.*

Typical chemical reactions, however, are influenced by a 10°C temperature change by a factor of 2.0. In many cases, the temperature effect on leaf movements can be observed only in the first few cycles, after which there seems to be a compensation so that time is measured about the same as it was at the original temperature. Such a compensation would seem to indicate some sort of chemical feedback, if the timing process is a chemical one. In many instances, the effects of temperature on biological timing are far less than in the case mentioned above; for example, 10°C temperature changes may influence timing by a factor of only 1.02 or even less in a few cases.

Chemistry of timing. In most instances, plant functions can be discussed in terms of chemistry, but biological timing has so far proved to be an exception to this general rule. There are no known chemical reactions that are as temperature-independent as is the biological-timing process. It may be that there is some sort of complex chemical feedback system that would account for this, but so far it has eluded our understanding.

The biological-timing phenomena in plants seems to be remarkably resistant to treatment with many chemicals. A number of compounds that cause harmful effects to plants will suppress the *expression* of the rhythm, but few will really change its *period*. Thus, lack of oxygen, excess carbon dioxide, various narcotics, and respiration inhibitors such as dinitrophenol, arsenate, cyanide, and fluoride cause the extent of leaf movement to be dampened, but the peaks of the rhythm are still separated by about 24 hours. These chemicals seem to inhibit processes that depend on the clock rather than inhibiting the clock itself. A few chemicals such as colchicine, ethyl carbamate (urethane) and cobaltous ion do change the period, but these chemicals are not effective in all systems.

SOME CURRENT PROBLEMS OF BIOLOGICAL TIME MEASUREMENT

Virtually nothing is known about the actual manner of operation of the biological clock. Some of the special problems are discussed below.

Is the clock internal (endogenous) or external (exogenous)? Virtually all investigators believe that the clock is located internally in the organism, but a few scientists still wonder whether the organism might not be responding to some very subtle environmental change other than light and temperature (which are usually held constant). Some experimenters have attempted to eliminate such factors as barometric pressure changes and daily cycles in cosmic ray intensity.

In one instance, the effect of the earth's rotation was nullified by placing plants on turntables on the South Pole! The turntables were rotated with a 24-hour period in a direction opposite to the earth. Other attempts to overcome the variability that accompanies the earth's rotation include airplane trips with trained bees from Paris to New York. None of these experiments changed the period of time measurement by the organism. There are still arguments in favor of the exogenous clock, but they have become increasingly less convincing with the completion of experiments such as those outlined above. Hence most workers feel that the clock is truly endogenous.

Does the clock operate like an hour glass or like a pendulum? In the case of rhythms such as leaf movements, the biological clock appears to be an oscillator, which, once it has been started, continues to measure out regular time intervals in a manner analogous to that of a pendulum. In photoperiodism, however, the organism seems to be measuring the length of the dark period (or perhaps the light period). In this case, it would be possible for the clock to be started anew each cycle during the change from light to dark (or vice versa). Thus the clock may be "wound up" by metabolism each day, in a manner somewhat similar to the effort required to turn over an hour glass. Once the sand has run through, however, effort must be applied again before it will start. This effort would be analogous to time measurement controlled by a chemical reaction. The speed of the reaction would be the means of measuring time, and, once the reaction had run through, new precursors would have to be provided before it could begin again. This question, like the first one, has not yet been answered to everyone's satisfaction, although most of the evidence seems to point toward an oscillating clock analogous to a pendulum. Such a clock is, however, more difficult to visualize in a living organism.

What is the nature of temperature independence in biological timing? This is probably part of the major question: "How does the clock operate?" At present we have a few theories that might explain temperature independence, but they are not yet based on sound experimental data.

Where is the clock located in the organism? Obviously it has to be within the cell, since single-celled organisms will exhibit the properties of time measurement. Furthermore, tissue cultures will also exhibit certain persistent circadian rhythms. At present, however, we have been completely unable to locate the clock within the cell with any degree of assurance. Evidence that it resides within the nucleus, for example, is countered by evidence that it does not.

How are the various timing phenomena interrelated? Since, in many instances, rhythms are superimposed on other rhythms, one asks whether there might be many clocks or only a single clock connected to the various functions through different gear trains, so to speak. A single plant may exhibit circadian rhythms, photoperiodism, and thermoperiodism. Is a single timer involved? It does seem possible, but unlikely, that one manifestation might be in response to an hour-glass type of clock, while another occurs only in response to an oscillator.

16

FLOWERING IN RESPONSE TO ENVIRONMENTAL CHANGE

One of the most intriguing steps in morphogenesis involves the formation of the flower. There are many aspects to the problem. First, does flowering occur in response to some change in the external environment? The answer for many species is an unqualified "yes." Second, what are the events that take place within the plant that translate some environmental condition into a redirection of growth? If the response is to light, what chemical factors inform the plant whether the lights are on or off? If flowering comes about in response to hormonal changes, what are these hormones and how are they synthesized? Third, what is floral differentiation? What happens at the meristematic sites when they stop growing vegetatively and become reproductive?

PHOTOPERIODISM

It is only in relatively recent years that we have been able to ask these questions properly. Up to 1920, most botanists felt that flowering occurred in response to soil nutrient conditions. We now know that this is a rather minor factor, and most of our conviction dates back to the revolutionary findings of W. W. Garner and H. A. Allard, which were published in 1920 (see Chapter 15). They found that in summer a variety of tobacco called Maryland Mammoth grew 10 feet tall but failed to flower at the latitude of Beltsville, Maryland (near Washington, D.C.). In winter, however, this plant flowered profusely in the greenhouse. In a series of carefully planned and executed studies, these U.S. Department of Agriculture scientists experimented to see whether light intensity, temperature, soil moisture, or day length could control flowering of this plant. Each of these factors was different in the winter greenhouses than in the summer fields. They were able to show that flowering could be controlled unequivocally by controlling day length, but other factors had no such effect. Plants placed in cabinets in the summer, so that they received short days and long nights, flowered profusely, whereas plants held under electric lights in the winter, so that they received long days and short nights, remained vegetative.

Garner and Allard extended their experiments to a number of other plants and found that most of the species investigated could be grouped into one of three classifications (Fig. 16-1); (1) short-day plants, such as Maryland Mammoth tobacco; (2) long-day plants, such as spinach, which responded in exactly the opposite way by flowering when the days were long and the nights were short; and (3) day-neutral plants, such as tomatoes, which flowered on both long and short days.

It should be emphasized that "short day" doesn't refer to short day in the usual sense. A short-day plant flowers when the day is *shorter than some maximum*. The cocklebur is a short-day plant and flowers when the day is *shorter* than about 15.6 hours, whereas henbane is a long-day plant, flowering when the days are *longer* than about 11 hours. Although one of these plants is a long-day plant and the other is a short-day plant, both flower when the days are between 11 and 15.3 hours long.

In the years since this pioneering work, complications have become apparent, although the basic story is still the same. It is now known that some plants do not require absolutely either long or short days in order to flower, but that flowering is promoted by one of these treatments. Furthermore, there are a few plant species that flower only on intermediate day lengths—when the days are neither too short nor too long. Some plants require, or are promoted by, a given day length only at a certain temperature, being day-neutral at other temperatures. A few species require long days followed by short days, and a few others require short days followed by long days.

VERNALIZATION

Temperature is almost always a complication in flowering. It may influence the day-length response, as indicated above, or it may directly influence the flowering process itself. An example is *vernalization*—the low-temperature requirement for flowering exhibited by many species. This response was known sometime before the studies of Garner and Allard, but few detailed investigations were carried out

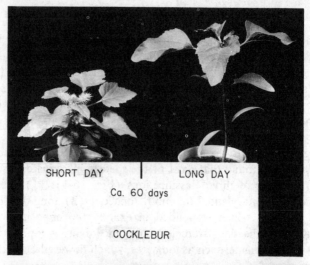

SHORT DAY | LONG DAY

Ca. 60 days

COCKLEBUR

SHORT DAY | LONG DAY

Ca. 110 days

TOMATO

Fig. 16-1. *The response of four selected plants to short days (8 hours light, 16 hours darkness or long days (20 hours light, 4 hours darkness). Numbers indicate approximate age of the plants. In the case of pigweed, flowering occurs so profusely on short day that if plants are grown under these conditions, they grow only an inch or two before their growth is stopped by the excessive number of flowers! Thus, in the example shown, the plant was held under long-day conditions until it had obtained a height of five or six inches, at which time it was placed under short-day conditions, resulting in flowering as shown. Reprinted with permission from Frank B. Salisbury,* The Flowering Process, *1963, Pergamon Press Limited.*

Fig. 16-1 *(continued)*.

until after the subject of flowering was suddenly made much more interesting by the report of the Beltsville workers.

Some cold-requiring species respond even when they are seeds. Moist seeds respond, but perfectly dry seeds do not. Usually the mature plant then requires a period of long days before flowering occurs. Long days alone do not cause flowering if the plants have not been subjected to a period of low temperature, nor does low temperature cause flowering unless it is followed by long days. The winter cereals (such as wheat or rye) are familiar examples.

Other species respond to low temperature only after they have reached some minimum size. Such a species may be a seedling, such as sugar beet with only one or a few leaves, or it may be a somewhat larger plant, such as henbane. In a number of cases, plants of this type flower in response to the low temperature alone, but in many cases the low-temperature treatment must be followed by long days if it is to be effective. In one case (*Chrysanthemum*), low temperature must be followed by short days.

The temperature optimum for vernalization is usually quite low, from 0° to 6° or 7°C, but often measurable vernalization effects can be observed at temperatures as high as 18°C. As in the case of the day-length response, it is not uncommon for the temperature promotion of flowering to be only a quantitative one; that is, certain plants will flower anyway, but they will do so much sooner if they are given a low-temperature treatment.

If plants are taken from the low-temperature conditions that induced them to flower and placed immediately under conditions of rather high temperature (35°C), the effects of the low-temperature treatment are often nullified. This process is called *devernalization*. It has been used rather extensively as a tool in studying the mechanisms of vernalization. For example, oxygen is required during the vernalization period, but devernalization will take place even in the absence of oxygen. This information gives us some insight into the biochemistry of vernalization. So far, however, we have only certain theories that may suggest further experiments. Perhaps some of the most encouraging work along these lines concerns the effects of applied chemicals. It has been possible in a few cases to promote flowering of certain cold-requiring species by soaking them in extracts obtained from already vernalized seeds. The active compounds in these extracts have not been positively identified, but they seem to be related to the nucleic acids. Furthermore, gibberellins usually cause cold-requiring plants to flower without a cold treatment.

PHOTOPERIODISM AND THE FLOWERING PROCESS

Many facts about flowering in response to day length have accumulated since 1920, and a few theories have been offered which attempt to relate and explain this factual material. At this time, however, we are still only on the threshold of gaining a complete understanding of the physiology of flowering. Some facts obtained and some areas of current research are summarized in the following paragraphs.

The Site of Response and the Hormonal Concept

Which part of the plant responds to day length? This is a relatively simple question to answer. We can darken the leaf, the stem, or the tip with black bags or black tape wrapped around the stem or petiole, providing short-day conditions for each plant part. When this is done, short-day plants flower only when the leaf is subjected to short days. Covering the stem or the tip never results in flowering. Long-day plants flower only when the leaf remains exposed. We are faced with an interesting situation: it is the shoot apical meristem that develops into the flower or inflorescence, but it is the leaf that responds to the environment. If the higher plant had a nervous system, this fact would be less surprising. As it is, we must probably look for some sort of chemical stimulus that is produced in the leaf in response to the environment and then translocated to the tip where flowering is initiated. If this stimulus is not a nutrient substance, or a combination of nutrient substances, then, by the definition given in Chapter 6, it must be a hormone.

There is no evidence that only nutrients are involved, but there is evidence for a hormone in the flowering process. When a plant that has been given the day-length conditions inducing it to flower is grafted to one that has not, the one that has not been induced often flowers as though it were receiving some sort of stimulus from the induced plant. This and still other experiments support the hormone concept of flowering response to day length. There is also excellent evidence that flower-*inhibiting* substances, produced under noninductive conditions, may also play a role. In some species these seem to control flowering, but more commonly there is an interaction between inhibitors and promoters.

It would seem that we should make extracts from induced plants, apply the extracts to noninduced plants, and wait for them to flower. This procedure has been tried countless times by many investigators all over the world, and, except in one or two recent cases (in which work is too preliminary for discussion here), such an experiment with short-day plants meets with failure. Gibberellins extracted from flowering long-day or cold-requiring plants, however, sometimes cause their vegetative counterparts to flower, but even here most workers doubt that gibberellins constitute the illusive flowering hormone (called *florigen*).

The Component Parts of the Flowering Process

A productive means of approaching the questions outlined in the introductory paragraph has been to try to divide the flowering process into a series of partial or component processes. Most of this work has been done with short-day plants, and indeed much of the work has been done with a single plant—the cocklebur (*Xanthium pennsylvanicum* Wall). This species has been used, perhaps more extensively than any other, because it responds to a single inductive cycle.

It was found rather early that the terms short-day and long-day are perhaps misleading. Most plants are influenced more by the length of the dark period than by that of the light period, as can be seen when plants are given cycles of light and dark that do not total 24 hours. Furthermore, if a dark period is interrupted by an interval of light, flowering of short-day plants is inhibited and flowering of long-day plants is promoted. Yet interrupting the light period with an interval of darkness has no effect, if the interval is fairly short (a few hours).

The cocklebur responds to a single period of darkness that is longer than about 8 hours and 20 minutes (8.3 hours). Furthermore, the cocklebur is a vigorous species; it can be defoliated to a single leaf with no apparent difficulties, and it is quite easy to handle in the greenhouse. As a result, it has been studied extensively and will be emphasized in the following discussion. A number of the responses of this plant are summarized in Fig. 16-2. Plants given a dark period of exactly the critical length (1) or shorter remain vegetative (leaf symbol). Plants given a dark period longer than this (2), preceded and followed by high-intensity light, form flowers and ultimately burs (bur symbol). When the long inductive dark period (the 12-hour dark period shown is arbitrary; others longer than 9 hours or so would also be effective) is preceded by a series of short dark periods separated by brief interruptions of light, the long dark period is not effective—unless it is separated from the short dark periods by a few hours of sunlight (4), or unless sugar is given during this period (5). Sugar is really only effective, however, when the short dark periods add up to about 24 hours (a complete cycle) but not when the light interruption is preceded by 8 hours of dark (6). But if 8 hours or so of light follow the 8 hours of dark, then the subsequent inductive dark period is effective. The light most effective in "resetting the clock" is red light (7), indicating that phytochrome must be in the F-phytochrome form during the light period if it is subsequently to be effective in the R-phytochrome form during the inductive dark period. A red-light interruption of the inductive dark period, especially at about 8 hours after the beginning (8), inhibits flowering, and this effect is reversed by following the red-light interruption immediately with far-red light (9). High temperatures applied for two hours or so have no effect during the first (time measurement) part of the dark period (10), but such a treatment will completely inhibit flowering when it is applied just after the critical night (11)—that is, during the first part of hormone synthesis. Some chemicals may inhibit flowering when they are applied during the dark period (12), but not when they are applied after the reactions of the dark period are complete (13). Examples are dinitrophenol and ethionine. Other chemicals inhibit flowering even when they are applied after the dark period (14). Some, such as the auxins, inhibit only during translocation of flowering hormone. Others, such as maleic hydrazide, inhibit growth of the bud regardless of when they are applied. In some experiments, a short dark period separated from the main inductive dark period by a brief light interruption (15) is inhibitory to flowering. This may be reversed by a few hours of sunlight (16) or by application of sugar (17).

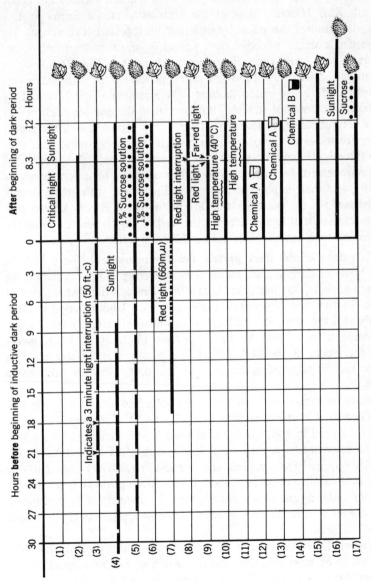

Fig. 16-2. *A summary of various photoperiodism experiments with the cocklebur, a short-day plant. (See text.)*

The high-intensity light process. Unless the single dark period used to induce the cocklebur plant is both preceded and followed by moderately bright light, flowering is either reduced or does not occur at all. Karl Hamner, now at the University of California at Los Angeles, studied this effect by means of an ingenious experiment. He preceded a single inductive dark period by short dark periods interspersed with very short light interruptions (see Fig. 16-1). Such treatment caused the following dark period to be completely ineffective. If the so-called flashing-light treatment were followed by about three hours of sunlight, however, then the ensuing dark period was fully effective. A few years later it was shown that if the plants were treated with sucrose, or other sugars or energy substrates, then the three-hour exposure to sunlight was not necessary. It appears that the requirement for high-intensity light is a requirement for photosynthesis, and that its purpose is to provide the leaf with ample energy substrates for the reactions that are to follow. It is now known that high-intensity red light preceding the dark period is also essential for biological time measurement during this dark period.

Reactions of the dark period: time measurement. Since at least 8.3 hours of darkness are required for flowering in the cocklebur, we must conclude that this plant is capable of measuring that interval of time. Furthermore, its ability to measure an 8.3 hour period is especially striking, since it is influenced at most only slightly by changes in temperature, at least over the range from 15° to 30°C. Yet to measure the length of the dark period, the plant's biochemistry must in some way be adjusted to the fact that it is dark. How does this come about?

Early investigators found that the effect of the dark period is nullified by a light interruption (see Fig. 16-1). The quantity (intensity multiplied by time) of light required for nullification was studied. If the interruption is very brief (for example, six seconds), the intensity required for complete effectiveness is relatively high (300 to 500 foot candles of white light). If the interruption is much longer (on the order of one to two hours), then the intensity of light required for complete effectiveness is much lower—approximately one foot candle or less.

The quality of light that is most effective was also studied. Red light proved to be most effective, and the action of red light could be reversed by far-red light. The flowering response to a light interruption is, then, mediated by the phytochrome-pigment system.

The equation on page 132 postulates that the pigment goes metabolically from F-phytochrome to R-phytochrome, even in the dark. This must be the case in flowering, since the high-intensity light preceding the dark period is usually richer in red than far-red, and phytochrome is much more sensitive to red anyway. Thus, the phytochrome must exist primarily as F-phytochrome when the dark period begins, although it is red light that causes the inhibition sometime later, indicating that the pigment has changed to R-phytochrome. The time required for this conversion might be equal to the 8.3 hours, but available evidence indicates that it is much shorter. Apparently the pigment system acts in some way to couple some other time-measuring mechanism within the plant with the environment. This mechanism might well be the oscillating timer, which controls circadian rhythms such as leaf movements. The relative temperature independence of the two phenomena suggests, for example, that both may be under control of the same biological clock.

Reactions of the dark period: synthesis of flowering hormone. If different groups of plants are given dark periods of different lengths, and the buds are examined some days later, it is found that the more the dark period exceeds 8.3 hours, the larger are the buds. The buds can be classified according to size and development (floral stages), as illustrated in Fig. 16-3. If groups of plants that have received different dark-period lengths are classified in this way, and the average floral stage is plotted against the length of the dark period, curves such as those in Fig. 16-4 result. Probably the best way to interpret these curves is with the hypothesis that a significant amount of flowering hormone begins to be synthesized at approximately 8.3 hours after the beginning of the dark period. As the length of the dark period increases, the amount of hormone synthesized increases quite rapidly at first and then much more slowly. We know that this synthesis of flowering hormone requires active respiration, and there is some evidence indicating that it might be related to the synthesis of steroids or of protein or peptides.

Translocation of flowering hormone. Usually after the plants are returned to the light, the flowering hormone is translocated from the leaf to the bud. Apparently some hormone can be translocated even if plants are in the dark, but hormone translocation normally takes place only after plants have been returned to the light. This fact can be demonstrated by performing a rather simple experiment. Plants are prepared in advance by removing all but one leaf. They are then given an inductive dark period, and, immediately following, the single leaf on some of these plants is removed. A little while later, leaves are removed from another group of plants, and still later from another group, and so on. A few days later the buds are examined, and the average floral stage is plotted as a function of the time when the

Vegetative

Stage 0   Stage 1   Stage 2   Stage 3

Stage 4   Stage 5   Stage 6

Stage 7   Stage 8

0.0   0.5   1.0mm

Fig. 16-3. *The stages of development through which a male (staminate) cocklebur bud progresses, beginning about 2.5 days after an inductive dark period. Stage 8 may be reached by the ninth to twelfth day after induction.*

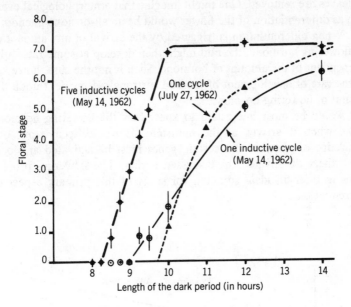

Fig. 16-4. *Three experiments showing floral stage as a function of night length. The actual length of the critical night depends somewhat on experimental conditions (such as temperature and light intensity before and after the dark period and temperature during the dark period—especially with a single cycle (two curves on the right); with more than one cycle (left curve), the 8.3 hour critical night is always approached very closely. Vertical lines indicate standard error.*

leaves were removed, producing curves such as those in Fig. 16-5. If leaves are removed immediately following the dark period, plants usually remain vegetative. If a number of hours (usually at least 24) are allowed to elapse after the end of the dark period, removal of the leaves scarcely inhibits flowering at all. It would seem that when leaves are removed immediately following the dark period, the flowering hormone has not been translocated out, and it is removed with the leaves. Twenty-four hours later all of the hormone is out of the leaf, and removing the leaf has very little effect on flowering. Intermediate defoliation times produce intermediate degrees of flowering (rates of development of the floral bud).

Differentiation and development of the bud. The experiments described above seem to indicate that the size of the flowering bud depends on the amount of flowering hormone exported from the leaf.

In the first case (see Fig. 16-4), different amounts of hormones are exported, depending on the length of the dark period. In the second case (see Fig. 16-5), different amounts are exported, depending on when the leaves are removed. One might imagine that a morphological event such as differentiation of the flower would be an all-or-none phenomenon. When differentiation is triggered by the arrival of any amount of the flowering hormone, the bud might then develop at some rate quite independent of the amount of hormone. Such is not the case, however, for the rate of development of the bud is strongly dependent upon the amount of flowering hormone.

It would be most interesting to know how the flowering hormone works when it arrives at the meristem. It would seem from our knowledge of genetics that certain genes must be activated and perhaps others deactivated, as discussed earlier. The flowering process seems to offer an ideal situation for study of this primary aspect of differentiation.

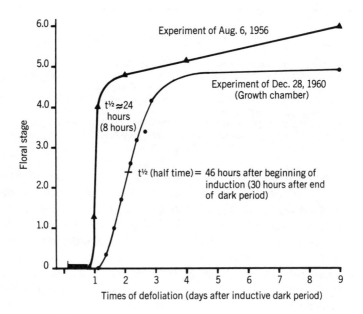

Fig. 16-5. *Two curves, indicating translocation of the flowering hormone, obtained by removing leaves at various times (abcissa) in relation to a single inductive dark period and then measuring floral stage 9 days later (ordinate). The two curves show two experiments, representing observable extremes. Low temperatures and low light intensities result in slow translocation.*

17

THE FRUIT

AND SEED

TYPES OF FRUITS

The matured ovary, normally containing one or more seeds, and *sometimes* including other closely related floral parts such as the perianth or the receptacle, constitute the *fruit.* If the fruit is derived from a single ovary (the ovary itself may be simple or compound) it is a *simple* fruit. Simple fruits are of two types: those that have a dry, membranous ovary wall (*pericarp*) at maturity, and those that are fleshy and succulent at maturity. The pericarp in fleshy fruits includes three well-differentiated layers: an outer *exocarp,* a middle *mesocarp,* and an inner *endocarp.* Usually in fleshy fruits, the mesocarp, or the mesocarp plus the endocarp, becomes succulent. Dry, simple fruits may be subdivided into those that open or *dehisce* at maturity and those that do not. The following diagram summarizes the various types of simple fruits.

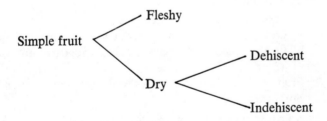

If the fruit is derived from several or many separate ovaries contained in a single flower, it is an *aggregate fruit,* in contrast to a *multiple fruit,* which originates from many ovaries contained in many different flowers. The following dichotomous key may be utilized to classify the various types of fruits.

I. Fruit derived from a single ovary (plus the floral tube in the case of the *pome*).

A. Ovary wall dry and membranous at maturity.

   1. Fruit dehiscent at maturity.

      a. Fruit derived from a simple ovary.

         (1) Fruit dehiscing along a single suture at maturity (*follicle*).

         (2) Fruit dehiscing along two sutures at maturity (*legume*).

      b. Fruit derived from a compound ovary.

         (1) Ovary consisting of two halves that separate at maturity, seeds attached to septum between the two halves (*silique*).

         (2) Ovary consisting of three or more carpels that separate or open at maturity (*capsule*).

   2. Fruit indehiscent at maturity.

      a. Pericarp hard and stony, seed not fused to the ovary wall (*nut*).

      b. Seed fused to the ovary wall, pericarp usually not hard and stony.

         (1) Seed fused to the ovary wall at one point only.

            (a) Pericarp extended into a wing-like outgrowth (*samara*).

            (b) Pericarp not extended into a wing-like outgrowth (*achene*).

         (2) Seed completely fused to the ovary wall (*caryopsis or grain*).

B. Ovary wall fleshy at maturity.

   1. Fruit derived from the pericarp only.

      a. Ovary simple and one-seeded, endocarp stony (*drupe*).

      b. Ovary compound, many-seeded, endocarp not stony (*berry*).

   2. Fruit derived from the ovary wall and the surrounding floral tube (*pome*).

II. Fruit derived from two or more ovaries.

   A. Fruit derived from many separate ovaries in a single flower (*aggregate fruit*).

   B. Fruit derived from many ovaries in separate flowers (*multiple fruit*).

Dry Simple Fruits

Dehiscent fruits. The *follicle* is a dry simple fruit derived from a simple ovary that splits open (dehisces) along one side at maturity.

The pods of milkweed and larkspur are examples of follicles. The *legume* is similar to the follicle except that legumes split along two sides at maturity. The fruit of the bean and the pea are legumes. Members of the mustard family (*Cruciferae*) produce an unusual type of dry, dehiscent fruit derived from a compound ovary known as a *silique,* in which the fruit separates into two halves at maturity, leaving the seeds attached to a dry upright septum. The *capsule* is a dry dehiscent fruit derived from a compound ovary and opening in a number of different ways, such as by pores in the top or by longitudinal slits in the sides. The fruit of the poppy, yucca, and lily are examples of various types of capsules.

Indehiscent fruits. *Nuts* are dry indehiscent fruits with a hard, tough pericarp; they contain a single seed that is not united to the ovary wall. Such structures as beechnut and hazelnut are true nuts. Dry, indehiscent, single-seeded fruits in which the ovary wall and the outer seed coat are fused at one point only are of two types: the *achene* and the *samara.* The two differ in that the pericarp of the samara is extended into a wing-like outgrowth. The fruit of the sunflower and buttercup are typical achenes, whereas the maple and ash trees produce samaras. The *grain* or *caryopsis* is the characteristic fruit of members of the grass family such as corn, wheat, and barley, and is similar to an achene except that the pericarp and seed coat are united all the way around, not at merely one point.

Fleshy Simple Fruits

A *drupe* is a fleshy one-seeded fruit in which the exocarp is membranous, the mesocarp is thick and succulent, and the endocarp is hard and stony. Such fruits as peaches, cherries, and apricots are typical drupes (also termed "stone" fruits). When both the mesocarp and the endocarp are fleshy and the ovary is compound, the fruit is a *berry.* Typical berries are the tomato and the grape. A special type of berry is the *hesperidium,* characterized by citrus fruits such as orange and grapefruit, in which the exocarp and mesocarp form a tough, leathery rind or "peel." Another special type of berry is the *pepo,* in which the exocarp along with some accessory tissue (the receptacle) form a hard, outer rind. Such fruits as the cucumber and the cantaloupe represent this type.

Accessory, Aggregate, and Multiple Fruits

The apple and the pear are pomes. This type of fruit is derived from the ovary *and* the floral tube; hence, it is often referred to as an *accessory* fruit. Most of the edible part of an apple or pear is ripened floral-tube tissue, not matured pericarp.

Aggregate fruits are really clusters of simple fruits, often associated with ripened accessory tissue. For example, the strawberry, a typical aggregate fruit, is a cluster of achenes embedded in a fleshy, ripe receptacle. Other types of aggregate fruits are the blackberry and the raspberry. Multiple fruits also may be considered as groups of simple fruits united, at least superficially, into a single structure. Examples of multiple fruits are the fig and the pineapple.

Parthenocarpy

Normally, the development of the fruit from an ovary into the mature, ripe structure is triggered by, and occurs simultaneously with, the development of the ovule into a mature seed. In certain rare cases, such as the navel orange and the banana, the fruit develops into a mature organ *without* concomitant seed development. This process is known as *parthenocarpy* and results in the formation of seedless fruit.

THE SEED

The seed is the characteristic reproductive structure. It is universally produced not only by flowering plants (angiosperms) but also by the various types of cone-bearing plants and their close relatives (gymnosperms). A seed consists essentially of three parts: (1) an extremely small diploid plant, the *embryo;* (2) abundant reserve food, either in the form of *endosperm* tissue or stored in the cotyledons of the embryo; and (3) a tough, hard protective covering, the *seed coat.*

The integuments of the ovule become the inner and outer seed coats. In addition, the other various morphologic structures externally associated with the ovule, such as the *micropyle* and the *funiculus,* are often represented in the mature seed. For example, in the seed of the ordinary garden bean, the micropyle is present as a small, circular depression on the concave side of the seed. Just above the micropyle is a large, oblong scar, the *hilum,* representing the area of attachment of the funiculus to the ovule. A part of the funiculus is fused to the outer integument, forming a conspicuous ridge, the *raphe.* Other specialized external structures may also be present. In the castor bean seed, the hilum, micropyle, and raphe are easily identifiable. In addition, the castor bean seed has at its base a large, spongy mass of tissue, the *caruncle,* which is a part of the outer seed coat.

The embryo of the seed develops from the zygote formed during double fertilization and hence is the new diploid or sporophyte plant. At the time the seed is disseminated, the embryo consists of the following parts: an embryonic root, the *radicle;* an embryonic shoot, the *plumule;* and one seed leaf or cotyledon (in the monocotyledons), two (in the dicotyledons), or many (in certain gymnosperms) attached to the seedling axis below the plumule and above the radicle. The part of the axis immediately below the cotyledons, forming a transition zone between plumule and radicle, is the *hypocotyl*. In the case of a monocotyledonous embryo such as that exemplified by corn or wheat, two additional structures are present, the *coleoptile* and the *coleorhiza*. The coleoptile is a hollow, cone-shaped structure that surrounds and encloses the plumule. The coleorhiza is a sheath of tissue surrounding and enclosing the radicle. In addition, the single cotyledon of the grain embryo is called the *scutellum* (Fig. 17-1).

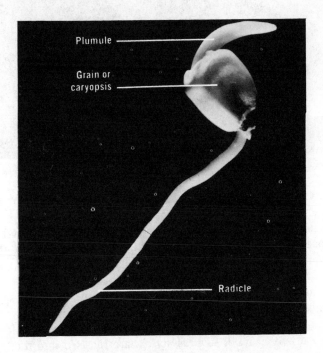

Plumule

Grain or caryopsis

Radicle

Fig. 17-1. *Corn seedling. Twice natural size.*

In many types of seeds, castor bean and corn for example, the primary endosperm cell gives rise to the food-storage tissue or endosperm of the seed. In many angiosperms, the endosperm is triploid in contrast to the diploid embryo. During the development of the embryo in seeds such as bean and pea, the endosperm is absorbed. At maturity, such seeds have no endosperm. In such cases, large amounts of food are stored in the large, fleshy cotyledons of the embryo.

When seeds such as the garden bean germinate, the cotyledons are thrust above the soil surface as a result of rapid elongation of the

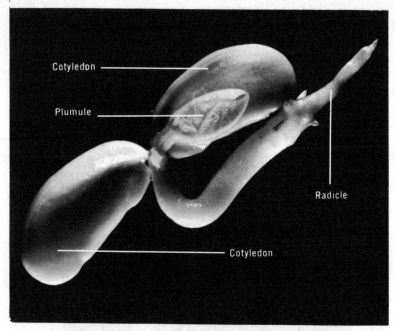

Cotyledon

Plumule

Radicle

Cotyledon

Fig. 17-2. *Garden bean seedling. Three times natural size.*

hypocotyl. (Fig. 17-2). In such cases, the bean cotyledons turn green, but otherwise change little. The castor bean seedling develops in a similar manner, except that the cotyledons of this plant expand into foliar organs closely resembling foliage leaves. The hypocotyl of the pea embryo does not elongate during seedling development. As a result, the cotyledons remain below the soil surface.

The cotyledon or scutellum of the grass embryo deserves special mention. This structure is highly specialized as an organ of digestion and food absorption. The various enzymes that are necessary for the digestion of stored food, such as starch, are released into the endosperm by cells of the scutellum. The soluble food substances that result from the activity of the enzymes are then absorbed by the scuttellum and translocated to regions of utilization within the growing seedling.

18

THE PHYSIOLOGY

OF GERMINATION

The morphology of a seed is impressive. Its entire structure is an adaptation to the resting condition and subsequent germination. Much more subtle and difficult to detect, but at least equally impressive, is the special set of functions of the seed. These often result in germination only under environmental conditions that will ensure the future growth of the seedling.

THE CONCEPT OF DORMANCY

All seeds require suitable moisture and temperature conditions for germination and subsequent growth of the seedling. Until such conditions are provided, the seed will remain *quiescent,* carrying on a very low level of metabolism and remaining alive, but not beginning the metabolic changes that will ultimately lead to cell division, growth, and emergence of the embryo. Other seeds are even more restrictive in their requirements for germination. Some of them may require special light treatments or conditions, some require the breaking of the seed coat, some require specific temperature treatments, and some require leaching by relatively large amounts of water for removal of chemical inhibitors. Seeds with these special requirements (in addition to ample moisture and proper temperature) are said to be *dormant* until the requirements have been met. Seeds requiring only moisture and proper temperature are said to be *quiescent* (but not *dormant*) before germination.

LIFE SPAN OF SEEDS

How long will a seed remain *viable?* That is, how long can a seed remain in the quiescent or the dormant condition and still be able to germinate when environmental conditions are finally suitable? One often hears about corn or wheat seeds taken from the tombs of Egypt, or the pueblos of southwestern United States, which can be planted and produce normal plants even though the seeds are thousands of years old. Apparently there is little truth in such stories. In a few cases, seed collected from Indian caves in the southwestern United States was not thousands of years old, but had been placed there quite recently by packrats! No suitably authenticated story of ancient but viable seeds is known.

A number of experiments have been carried out, or at least initiated, in an attempt to determine life span. Seeds are stored under moist and dry, warm and cold, and perhaps other conditions, and at intervals extending over many years samples are removed for the determination of viability. Some of the experiments have been in progress for more than half a century, and we can begin to draw some conclusions. It appears that only a very few seeds can exceed a maximum life span of about 50 years. Some are known to have an extremely short life span measured in days, such as orchid, tea, and certain willow seeds. A 10-year life span is quite common, and a few seeds will live up to 50 years. The life spans for wheat and corn are in the neighborhood of 30 to 50 years. Life spans are longest under dry, cool conditions.

One authenticated case of extremely long-lived seeds is known. This involves the large, extremely hard seed of the lotus plant in China. Lotus seeds are found deeply imbedded in layers of peat, and their age can be determined by their position in the peat bog and by radioactive-carbon dating. Such seeds, treated to break the seed coat and then planted, have been known to germinate even though they are at least eight hundred, and perhaps more than two thousand, years old.

THE LIGHT REQUIREMENT FOR GERMINATION

As noted in Chapter 14, some seeds require special light treatments for germination. In the most-studied instances, orange-red light promotes germination, provided that the seeds have first been allowed to take up a certain amount of moisture, and provided temperature conditions during germination are within the proper range. Temperature during the period of illumination itself is unimportant, as one might expect of a light-driven reaction. Everyone knows that temperature corrections do not have to be made in the exposure settings when one takes photographs in extremely hot or extremely cold weather. The promotion by orange-red light is reversed by far-red light, and this process is repeatedly reversible.

In addition to this fundamental response, other light responses are known. There are, for example, seeds that are *inhibited* in their germination by a light treatment. A few seeds are also known to respond to the *duration* of the light treatment, in a manner very analogous to the flowering response controlled by day or night length. Certain kinds of birch seeds are long-day seeds, in that they germinate when the day length exceeds some minimum or the night length is less than some maximum. At least one short-day seed is also known (nemophila). These are good examples of photoperiodism.

In a few instances, blue light is known to have an effect on germination. The interpretation of this phenomenon is not yet clear, but it may be related to the phytochrome-controlled germination. In many germination studies, special chemical substances that inhibit or promote germination have been postulated to be a part of the mechanism. In a few cases, such substances have actually been extracted and studied, but in most cases they have only been inferred. Some investigators think that the proper light treatment results in the production of a germination promoter, or perhaps the destruction of a germination inhibitor. This must be true if we think of the phytochrome itself, but it may be that phytochrome, in one of its two forms (probably F-phytochrome), leads to the production of other, more specific germination inhibitors or promoters. Seeds having a light requirement for germination make particularly good weeds. They may lay dormant in the ground for years until they are brought into the light by plowing.

SCARIFICATION

In many seeds, germination will not occur until the seed coat has been broken. This process is called *scarification*. The hard seed coat may serve to keep water or oxygen out of the seed, or in a few cases it may be so hard that it keeps the embryo in. Many seeds have this feature, including a number of the legumes and mallows (such as hollyhocks). Seeds of the black locust (a legume) are sometimes used in classroom demonstrations. Intact seeds will not germinate when planted, but seeds passed around the classroom in a bottle that is shaken by each student become scarified and will germinate.

Scarification may be brought about in the laboratory by nicking the seed with a knife or a file, or by treating it with sulfuric acid or organic solvents (which apparently dissolve certain fatty substances that otherwise keep the water out), or even by boiling for a short time.

In nature, the requirement for scarification is of obvious value. If a seed must be scarified, it cannot germinate when it first drops from the mother plant; it must wait until the forces of nature have had time to break the seed coat. Hence germination will not occur in the fall but only in the following spring, after scarification has occurred and when temperature conditions are favorable.

Scarification in nature is brought about by a number of forces. The smoke tree of our southwestern deserts germinates only after the seeds have been washed down the dry desert gullies by a cloudburst. If they are carried too far in the flood, they will be ground to pieces, and if they are not carried far enough, scarification will be incomplete and they will not germinate. Often a number of smoke trees can be found about 300 yards below the parent trees at the head of a gully. A cloudburst sufficient to carry the seeds this distance provides ample moisture in the soil for the subsequent growth of the seedlings.

In some instances, birds may bring about scarification by passing seeds through their alimentary canal, and in a few cases, such as the frequently burned chaparral of Mediterranean climates, fire is required to break the seed coat, ensuring the rapid germination of many seeds as soon as sufficient moisture is available following a fire. Most commonly, scarification is brought about by the normal processes of decay. In one carefully studied instance, a specific fungus was required for scarification of saltbrush (*Atriplex confertifolia*) seed in the Utah desert. This appears to be an example of mutual benefit between two organisms, or *symbiosis:* the seed provided a substrate for growth of the fungus, which in turn allowed germination of the seed.

STRATIFICATION

Some seeds, including many rosaceous ones, require an extended period of cold before they will germinate. This characteristic is also of obvious survival value, since such seeds will not germinate in the fall but only the following spring. They must be treated with low temperatures (0° to 10°C) while they are in the moist condition, usually for a number of months. In horticultural practice, layers of flats containing the moist seed are left outside during the winter, or perhaps placed in a cold-storage room. This process is called *stratification.*

Dormancy mechanisms, such as the cold or scarification requirement, prolong the period before germination, and it is said that the seed is undergoing *after-ripening* during this period. Perhaps the term is of less value to us now that we are gaining some understanding of the mechanisms involved. The requirement for cold may be in addition to a requirement for scarification, or conceivably even for particular light or other environmental conditions.

CHEMICAL INHIBITORS OF GERMINATION

The seeds in a tomato, orange, or melon normally germinate readily when planted in the ground. In these fruits they are certainly subjected to ideal moisture and temperature conditions, and one might ask why they fail to germinate (most of us have occasionally observed a germinating orange seed in the fruit, but such occurrences are relatively rare). It can be demonstrated that these seeds remain dormant in response to chemical substances present in the fruits themselves.

Other instances of germination inhibitors are also known. Many seeds will not germinate until they have been leached extensively by running water. Again, the value of such a requirement under natural conditions is not difficult to discern. A seed will germinate only after a rather heavy rainstorm that is capable of removing its chemical inhibitor and wetting the ground to a considerable depth. In the desert, some seeds require perhaps half an inch of rainfall before their inhibitors are removed so that they can germinate. A lesser amount does not bring about germination, nor do a number of short rains separated by intervals of time. Apparently the level of the inhibitor is reestablished in the seed following a short rain and is maintained until enough rain comes at one time to remove the inhibitor and thoroughly wet the soil. In a few instances, the chemical nature of the inhibitor has been determined. The saltbrush in the Utah desert contains sodium chloride in quantities sufficient to inhibit its germination until it has been leached out by the spring rains. This is in addition to the requirement for scarification by the specific fungus. Organic compounds that inhibit germination are also known in seeds.

In many instances, mature plants produce compounds that inhibit the germination of seeds. Such compounds might properly be called antibiotics, since they are produced by one organism and are toxic to another. This is an example of a sort of chemical warfare, in which one plant is able to limit the competition from other plants by the production of specific chemical substances. Usually these substances are produced in the leaves and only reach the soil after the leaves fall to the ground and decay.

DELAYED EMBRYO DEVELOPMENT

One other dormancy mechanism appears to be a matter of the time it takes for the embryo to complete its development after the seed has been separated from the mother plant. That is, some seeds (notably holly, *Ginkgo,* and *Gnetum*) will not germinate when they are first collected from the mother plant, simply because they are not yet "ripe." The only way to overcome the dormancy of these seeds is to allow sufficient time for the embryo to become mature.

Anderson, E. *Plants, Man and Life*. Boston: Little, Brown and Company, 1952.

Annual Review of Plant Physiology. Palo Alto, Calif.: Annual Reviews, Inc.

Audus, L. J. *Plant Growth Substances*, 2nd ed. New York: Interscience Publishers, 1960.

Bailey, I. W. *Contributions to Plant Anatomy*. Waltham, Mass.: Chronica Botanica Company, 1954.

Bold, H. C. *The Plant Kingdom*. Englewood Cliffs, N.J.: Prentice-Hall, Inc., 1960.

Bonner, J. F., and A. W. Galston. *Principles of Plant Physiology*. San Francisco: W. H. Freeman & Company, 1952.

Bünning, E. *The Physiological Clock*. New York: Academic Press, Inc., 1964.

Carlquist, S. J. *Comparative Plant Anatomy*. New York: Holt, Rinehart and Winston, Inc., 1961.

Clowes, F. A. L. *Apical Meristems*. Philadelphia: F. A. Davis Company (Blackwell Scientific Publications), 1961.

Crafts, A. S. *Translocation in Plants*. New York: Holt, Rinehart and Winston, Inc., 1961.

De Robertis, E. D. P., et al. *General Cytology*, 3rd ed. Philadelphia: W. B. Saunders Company, 1960.

Eames, A. J. *Morphology of the Angiosperms*. New York: McGraw-Hill Book Company, Inc., 1961.

——————. *Morphology of Vascular Plants, Lower Groups*. New York: McGraw-Hill Book Company, Inc., 1936.

——————, and L. H. MacDaniels. *An Introduction to Plant Anatomy*, 2nd ed. New York: McGraw-Hill Book Company, Inc., 1947.

Esau, K. *Anatomy of Seed Plants*. New York: John Wiley & Sons, Inc., 1960.

——————. *Plant Anatomy*. New York: John Wiley & Sons, Inc., 1953.

——————. *Plants, Viruses, and Insects*. Cambridge: Harvard University Press, 1961.

Evans, L. T., ed. *Environmental Control of Plant Growth: Proceedings of a Symposium Held at Canberra, Australia*. New York: Academic Press, Inc., 1963.

Foster, A. S., and E. M. Gifford, Jr. *Comparative Morphology of Vascular Plants*. San Francisco: W. H. Freeman & Company, 1959.

Galston, A. W. *The Life of the Green Plant.* Englewood Cliffs, N.J.: Prentice-Hall, Inc., 1961.

Hillman, W. S. *The Physiology of Flowering.* New York: Holt, Rinehart and Winston, Inc., 1962.

Hutchins, R. E. *This Is a Leaf.* New York: Dodd, Mead & Company, 1962.

International Conference on Plant Growth Regulation (4th), Yonkers, N.Y., 1959. *Plant Growth Regulation.* Ames: Iowa State University Press, 1961.

Jensen, W. A. *Botanical Histochemistry: Principles and Practice.* San Francisco: W. H. Freeman & Company, 1962.

——————, and L. G. Kavaljian, eds. *Plant Biology Today: Advances and Challenges.* Belmont, Calif.: Wadsworth Publishing Company, Inc., 1963.

Knobloch, I. W., ed. *Selected Botanical Papers.* Englewood Cliffs, N.J.: Prentice-Hall, Inc., 1963.

Lee, A. E., and C. Heimsch. *Development and Structure of Plants: A Photographic Study.* New York: Holt, Rinehart and Winston, Inc., 1962.

Mayer, A. M., and A. Poljakoff-Mayber. *The Germination of Seeds.* New York: The Macmillan Company, 1963.

Meeuse, B. J. D. *The Story of Pollination.* New York: The Ronald Press Company, 1961.

Metcalfe, C. R. *Anatomy of the Monocotyledons.* New York: Clarendon Press, 1960.

——————, and L. Chalk. *Anatomy of the Dicotyledons.* 2 vols. New York: Clarendon Press, 1950.

Preston, R. D., ed. *Advances in Botanical Research.* New York: Academic Press, Inc., 1963.

Runland, W., ed. *Encyclopedia of Plant Physiology.* Berlin: Springer-verlag, 1955.

Salisbury, F. B. *The Flowering Process.* New York: Pergamon Press, Inc., 1963.

Scientific American. (Contains many articles of current botanical interest.)

Scientific American, eds. *The Physics and Chemistry of Life.* New York: Simon and Schuster, Inc., 1955.

——————. *Plant Life.* New York: Simon and Schuster, Inc., 1957.

Siegel, S. M. *The Plant Cell Wall.* New York: Pergamon Press, Inc., 1962.

Sinnott, E. W. *Plant Morphogenesis.* New York: McGraw-Hill Book Company, Inc., 1960.

Steere, W. C., ed. *Fifty Years of Botany: Golden Jubilee Volume of the Botanical Society of America.* New York: McGraw-Hill Book Company, Inc., 1958.

Turrill, W. B., ed. *Vistas in Botany.* New York: Pergamon Press, Inc., 1959.

Wilson, G. B., and J. H. Monison. *Cytology.* New York: Reinhold Publishing Corp., 1961.

Abscission. The separation of plant parts such as leaves, twigs, or fruits from the plant body by the disintegration of a special layer of cells called the *abscission layer.*

Absolute humidity. The actual amount of water vapor in the air expressed as weight per unit volume, or as a vapor pressure.

Accumulation. The absorption of materials, usually ionic, by cells utilizing metabolic energy; typically occurs against a concentration gradient.

Achene. A dry, one-seeded, indehiscent fruit in which the seed coat is united to the pericarp at only one point.

Adnation. Union or fusion of unlike parts, such as petals and carpels in the flower.

Adsorption. The adhesion of a substance (such as water molecules or other molecules) to the surface of a solid (commonly a colloidal particle or the microfibrils of the cell wall).

Adventitious roots. Roots that originate in an unusual way, such as from mature stem or leaf tissue.

After-ripening. Changes taking place in a seed during storage or special treatment which allow subsequent germination to take place; changes relating to breaking of dormancy in seeds.

Allometric growth. Correlation in growth rates between different parts or dimensions of an organism; actual growth rates may be different and may change, but relative rates of the parts remain constant.

Alternate leaf arrangement. A single leaf per node.

Alternation of generations. The alternation of a diploid, spore-producing generation, the sporophyte, with a haploid, gamete-producing generation, the gametophyte, in the life history of a plant.

Androecium. The male part of the flower—all of the stamens collectively.

Angiosperm. One of the flowering plants (ovules enclosed in an ovary).

Annual ring. Growth rings in the secondary vascular tissues of the plant, formed on an annual basis.

Antagonism. Used in relation to ion uptake by plant cells or intact plants. When one ion inhibits the uptake of another, it is said to antagonize its uptake.

Anther. The fertile part of the stamen; the part that produces the pollen.

Antheridium. The male gametangium, consisting of a single specialized cell or group of cells in which the male gametes or sperm are borne.

Anthocyanins. Brightly colored, water-soluble plant pigments; usually red, blue, or violet. Usually occur in the vacuole.

Antipodals. Cells (usually three in number) of the embryo sac located in the end or part opposite the micropyle.

Apical meristems. Meristems borne at the tips of the vegetative organ.

Apoplast. The system of interconnected cell walls in the plant.

Archegonium. The multicellular female gametangium in which a single egg is borne.

Auxin. A generic term for compounds characterized by their capacity to induce stem elongation in certain standard tests such as Went's Curvature Test, or the Section Growth Test. May or may not be a naturally occurring compound.

Axil, leaf. The hypothetical angle formed between the stem and the adaxial surface of the leaf.

Bark. In woody stems, all of the tissues outside the vascular cambium.

Base (leaf). That part of the leaf blade adjacent to the petiole; in sessile leaves, that part of the leaf blade adjacent to the stem.

Berry. A simple, fleshy fruit in which the mesocarp and endocarp remain succulent.

Biennial. A plant that completes its life cycle in two years and then dies; normally remains as a vegetative rosette the first year, flowering the second year in response to the low temperatures of the intervening winter.

Biological clock. The mechanism within the cell allowing organisms to measure time; as exhibited by persistent rhythms, photoperiodism, etc.

Blade. The expanded or flattened part of the leaf.

Bundle sheath. Parenchyma cells (also sclerenchyma) organized in a sheath around the leaf veins.

Callus. A tumor-like tissue of thin-walled cells developing over wounds or in response to certain applied growth regulators.

Calyx. All of the sepals collectively; also, in a complete flower, the outermost whorl of parts.

Capillarity. The rise of water in small tubes, or pores, due to the meniscus which forms in response to adhesion between the water and the surface of the tube or pore.

Capsule. A dry, dehiscent fruit derived from two or more united carpels.

Carotenoids. Fat soluble plant pigments, usually red, orange, or yellow. Usually contained in chloroplasts.

Carpel. The female reproductive part of the flower. See also *pistil, simple.*

Caruncle. A spongy tissue mass at one end of a seed (such as castor bean).

Caryopsis. A dry, one-seeded, indehiscent fruit (a grain) in which the seed coat and pericarp are completely united.

Casparian strip. A suberized strip or lamella occurring on the radial, upper, and lower walls of endodermal cells.

Cell sap. The contents of the various vacuoles of the cell.

Centriole. A specialized cytoplasmic body occurring commonly in animal cells and occasionally in cells of lower plants. The centriole or centrosome divides during the prophase of meiosis or mitosis into two centrioles that become the poles of the spindle. This structure has not been identified in cells of higher plants.

Chloroplasts. Specialized plastids containing chlorophyll and functioning in photosynthesis.

Chromonema (pl. *chromonemata*). Thread-like proteinaceous bodies bearing genetically active material and giving rise to the chromosomes during mitosis and meiosis.

Chromoplasts. Specialized, colored plastids containing yellowish, orange, or red pigments such as xanthophyll and carotene.

Chromosomes. Definite nuclear bodies derived from the chromonemata, and bearing the genes. These structures are usually conspicuous during prophase and split longitudinally into chromatids during metaphase of mitosis.

Circadian rhythm. A rhythm approximating 24 hours in its period.

Coalescence. Union of like parts, such as petals fused to petals, etc.

Cohesion theory. The cohesion theory of the rise of sap in stems is based on the idea that the water columns in the stem are held together by cohesive forces.

Coleoptile. A hollow, cone-like organ surrounding and enclosing the plumule in seeds and seedlings of grasses.

Coleorhiza. A hollow, cone-like organ similar in structure to the coleoptile but surrounding and enclosing the radicle in the seeds and seedlings of grasses.

Collenchyma. A primary tissue composed of cells that are elongated and have thickened primary walls, usually functioning as living elements.

Colloids. Small particles that will pass through filter paper but not through cellophane membranes and that are visible only in the ultra or electron microscope; they exhibit certain properties, such as Brownian movement, formation of gels, cation exchange, and imbibition.

Companion cells. Living, thin-walled, nucleate cells closely associated with sieve-tube elements.

Complementary bonding. Applied to the spatial relationship between the two nucleotides constituting a pair, each in an opposite chain of the deoxyribonucleic acid, double-helix, molecule.

Cone. An aggregation of fertile leaves or sporophylls.

Cork. A suberized tissue, developed from the cork cambium of stems and roots; the commercial product secured from cork oak trees grown extensively in Southern Europe.

Cork cambium. A lateral meristem, formed in woody plants, which is responsible for the formation of cork tissue.

Cork tissue. A suberized tissue produced by the cork cambium.

Corpus. In shoot apices, the central part, in which planes of cell division are randomly oriented.

Corolla. The part of the flower made up of petals.

Cortex. Primary topographic tissue lying outside the vascular tissues and inside the epidermis in stems and roots.

Crown gall. A plant tumor occurring initially on the stem near the ground line (at the crown); caused by a bacterium.

Cuticle. A waxy layer formed on the outer, tangential walls of epidermal cells.

Cutin. A fatty, waxy substance closely related chemically to suberin. It forms a part of the outer tangential and radial walls of epidermal cells and makes up the cuticle.

Cytochromes. Metal-protein enzymes concerned with hydrogen (electron) transfer and combination of hydrogen with oxygen in respiration.

Dehiscent. Structures, such as fruits and anthers, that open at maturity.

Deoxyribonucleic acid (DNA). A complex molecule constituting the genes. The molecule is thought to be a double helix, consisting of two chains of nucleotides held together by complementary bonding.

Dermatogen. In roots, the primary meristematic tissue, synonymous with protoderm, that gives rise to the epidermis.

Determinate growth. Growth that is ultimately limited by the cessation of meristematic activity (for example, leaves or flowers as contrasted to the stem).

Dicotyledons. Plants in one subgroup of the angiosperms; characterized by two cotyledons in the embryo and by other features described in the text.

Differentially permeable. Applied to membranes that allow the passage of one substance at a faster rate than the passage of another substance.

Diffusion pressure deficit (*enter tendency*). The tendency for pure water at one atmosphere pressure to diffuse toward a given part of a system; expressed in pressure terms (atmospheres).

Dioecious. Having male and female reproductive organs on separate organisms.

Diploid. Having two sets of more or less identical chromosomes. Homologous pairs of chromosomes represent the diploid condition.

Double fertilization. The reproductive process in angiosperms whereby one sperm nucleus fuses with the female gamete or egg while the second sperm nucleus fuses with the two polar nuclei.

Drupe. A simple, fleshy fruit in which the endocarp becomes hard and stony, the mesocarp becomes fleshy and succulent, and the exocarp becomes a membranous skin.

Earlywood. During any given growth period, the xylem that is formed first by the vascular cambium. In those plants with annual rings, earlywood is equivalent to springwood.

Embryo. The young, multicellular sporophyte plant developed from the zygote.

Embryo sac. The female gametophyte plant in angiosperms, consisting in many examples of an eight-nucleate, seven-celled structure.

Endodermis. Specialized inner layer of the cortex characterized by cells with Casparian strips.

Endocarp. The innermost layer of the fruit wall or ovary wall.

Endogenous rhythm. A rhythm in some activity of an organism (such as leaf movements) which originates within the organism itself.

Endosperm. Nutrient tissue in the angiosperm seed or maturing ovule, usually triploid.

Enter tendency. Term used in relation to osmosis and other processes to describe in units of pressure the tendency for pure water at one atmosphere pressure to enter a given part of a system.

Enzyme. Protein substances functioning as catalysts in metabolic reactions.

Epidermis. The specialized outermost cell layer of the plant body, functioning as a protective tissue.

Epigynous. A floral condition in which the calyx, corolla, and androecium appear to arise from the top of the ovary. The ovary is said to be inferior.

Epinasty. Twisting or curling of plant leaves. or petioles, in response to uneven growth on opposite sides of the organ in question.

Etiolation. The condition of plants (usually angiosperms) grown in the dark, in which the stems greatly elongate, leaves fail to expand, and chlorophyll does not develop.

Exocarp. The outermost wall layer of the fruit or of the ovary.

Fascicular cambium. That part of the vascular cambium originating within a vascular bundle.

Fibers. Elongated, dead cells with thick lignified secondary walls functioning as strength and support.

Fibrous root system. A root system in which all the major units are approximately the same length and diameter.

Filament. The elongated, sterile part of the stamen.

File meristem. A meristem in which cell division is limited to a single plane.

Florigen. A flowering hormone, or stimulus, arising in some plants in response to an appropriate environmental treatment (such as long or short days).

Flower. An aggregation of modified fertile and sterile leaves making up the characteristic reproductive structure of angiosperms.

Flower, complete. A flower in which all four parts (calyx, corolla, androecium, and gynoecium) are present.

Flower, imperfect. A flower in which the androecium or the gynoecium is missing.

Flower, incomplete. Flowers in which one or more whorl or group of parts is missing.

Flower, perfect. A flower that contains both male and female reproductive organs.

Follicle. A simple, dry, dehiscent fruit derived from a single carpel and dehiscing along a single suture.

Foraminate. Containing circular openings or perforations.

Free energy. In our context, a property of a substance which may define its ability to diffuse; diffusion occurs along a gradient from high to low free energy. Factors influencing free energy are described in the text.

Free space. The part of a plant that is in free diffusion equilibrium with the external world (probably the cell walls and intercellular spaces).

Fruit. A matured ovary with or without accessory structures.

Fruit, accessory. A fruit that develops from an ovary or ovaries and, in addition, other part(s) of the flower, such as a floral tube or the receptacle.

Fruit, aggregate. A fruit (such as strawberries) derived from many separate carpels borne in a single flower and sometimes including accessory parts such as the receptacle or the calyx tube.

Fruit, multiple. A fruit (such as pineapple and fig) derived from many ovaries of many different flowers.

Fruit, simple. A fruit derived from a single ovary.

Funiculus. The stock that connects the ovule to the placenta of the ovary wall.

Fusiform cambial initials. Elongated cells making up a part of the vascular cambium and giving rise to the elongated cells of the secondary xylem and secondary phloem.

Gametangium. A unicellular or multicellular structure in which gametes (sex cells) are borne.

Gamete. The primary reproductive cells that fuse with each other to produce zygotes; a sex cell—sperm (male) and egg (female) cells.

Gametophyte. The organism arising from the products of a miotic division (spores); produces the gametes.

Gene. A unit of heredity controlling one or more hereditary characteristics; now known to be located on the chromosomes and to consist of nucleoprotein (the nucleic acid part, DNA, probably being most significant).

Generative nucleus. One of two nuclei found in the mature pollen grain; it divides mitotically to produce the two sperm nuclei.

Geotropism. Growth of plant parts *toward* (positive, as in roots) or *away from* (negative, as in stems) the earth's center of gravity.

Gibberellic acid. A growth substance particularly effective in causing stem elongation in intact plants.

Glycolysis. The respiratory breakdown of glucose (or starch, or fructose) to pyruvic acid.

Golgi (complex). A smooth membrane system found primarily in animal cells and thought to be associated with secretory activities.

Ground Meristem. The primary meristematic tissue that in stems gives rise to the cortex, pith, and medullary rays, and in roots to the cortex and endodermis.

Growth regulator. A substance active in controlling growth and development of plants; may be either synthetic or a naturally occurring compound.

Guard cells. Specialized epidermal cells surrounding stomata.

Guttation. The extrusion of water in liquid form by plants, usually through special structures called *hydathodes.*

Gymnosperm. A member of the group of plants characterized by having ovules not enclosed in an ovary (for example, conifers and related groups).

Gynoecium. The female part of the flower, made up of carpels.

Haploid. Having one set of chromosomes. No chromosome represented more than once in the set.

Heartwood. The entirely dead, inner xylem of a woody stem or root; often a different color from the living, functional xylem or sapwood.

Herb. A plant with no persistent woody stem above ground.

Herbaceous. Plant parts with little or no hard woody (secondary) tissue.

Herbicides. Chemical substances that kill plants. Selective herbicides (weed killers) kill some plants but not others.

Hesperidium. The type of berry in which the exocarp and mesocarp become leathery, forming a peel as in oranges, lemons, and other citrus fruit.

Hilum. A scar on the seed coat marking the place of attachment of the funiculus.

Hormone. An organic substance synthesized in one part of the organism and translocated to some other part, where it exercises a control in some phase of the growth process. It must be active in very small amounts.

Hydrophilic. Having an attraction for water, as cellulose surfaces or certain colloids.

Hypocotyl. The part of the seedling axis below the points of attachment of the cotyledon and above the radicle.

Hypogynous. Flowers in which the stamens, petals, and sepals are attached to the receptacle *below* the ovary.

Imbibition. The adsorption of water on or by hydrophilic surfaces.

Indehiscent. A fruit or anther that does not open at maturity.

Indeterminate growth. Growth that may continue indefinitely, such as from a terminal or lateral meristem.

Indusium. The tissue covering a fern sorus.

Initial. A meristematic cell that combines more or less continuous cell division with self-perpetuation.

Interfascicular cambium. That part of the vascular cambium in woody dicotyledons arising between discrete vascular bundles; together with the fascicular cambium, makes up the vascular cambium.

Internode. That part of a stem between two successive nodes.

Kinetic activity. The motion of molecular or atomic-sized particles; an expression of their kinetic energy.

Kinetics. Experiments in which some change (such as the response of a plant to an applied chemical) is studied as a function of time or as a function of concentration.

Kinetin. Six-furfurylamino-purine; a growth regulator that causes cell division and other responses in certain experimental situations.

Krebs cycle. The cyclic, respiratory breakdown of pyruvic acid (and some other compounds) to carbon dioxide and water.

Lateral meristems. Meristems, such as the vascular cambium and the cork cambium, that produce the secondary plant body; located on the sides of stems and roots.

Latewood. The xylem formed last in a given growth period. In species forming annual rings, latewood is synonymous with summerwood.

Leaf. The flattened, dorsiventral vegetative organ consisting of a distal blade (the flattened part) and a proximal petiole, concerned primarily with photosynthesis.

Leaf, compound. A leaf in which the blade is subdivided into two or more leaflets.

Leaf, simple. A leaf with only one blade.

Legume. A simple, dry, dehiscent fruit splitting along two sutures.

Leucoplasts. Colorless plastids often associated with food storage.

Logarithmic growth phase. That phase of the growth of a plant in which the growth rate (unit increase in plant volume per interval of time) is directly proportional to size of the plant: the larger a plant is during this phase, the faster it grows.

Mass meristem. A meristem in which cell division occurs in all planes.

Medullary rays. Parenchyma tissue extending from the pith to the cortex in between the vascular bundles in the stems of various dicotyledons.

Megagametophyte. See *embryo sac.*

Megaspore. A haploid cell or nucleus occurring within a megasporangium and giving rise to the megagametophyte or, in the case of angiosperms, to the embryo sac.

Megaspore mother cell. The one diploid cell in each ovule that will undergo meiosis.

Meiosis. Nuclear division that reduces diploid nuclei to the haploid condition.

Meristem. Any group of cells capable of more or less continuous cell division.

Mesocarp. The middle layer of the fruit wall or of the ovary wall.

Metabolism. The sum total of all chemical activities of a living organism (synthesis and breakdown of the substance and products of protoplasm).

Microgametophyte. See *pollen grain.*

Micropyle. The opening or pore in the integuments of the ovule, persisting as a small perforation in the seed coat.

Microspore. A haploid nucleus or cell that gives rise to the male gametophyte; in the case of angiosperms, the immature pollen grain.

Middle lamella. The first wall layer, formed by dividing plant cells and occurring between the subsequently formed primary cell walls of daughter cells.

Mitochondria. Spherical or rod-shaped cytoplasmic bodies concerned primarily with respiration and energy transfer in the cell. These structures are quite small but are visible with the light microscope.

Mitosis. Nuclear division that results in the formation of two daughter nuclei (or cells) exactly like the mother cell.

Monocotyledon. Plants in one subgroup of the angiosperms; characterized by one cotyledon in the embryo and by other features described in the text.

Monoecious. Having incomplete flowers borne at separate places on a single organism.

Morphogenesis. The origin of form; the processes of cell division, growth, and differentiation which result in the complex, adult organism.

Node. A place on a stem where one or more leaves are attached.

Nuclear membrane. The double-membrane system enclosing the nucleus.

Nuclear sap. The viscous, hyaline fluid found inside the nuclear membrane.

Nucleic acid. Made up of smaller molecules called nucleotides. Deoxyribonucleic acid (DNA) is found only in cell nuclei (chromosomes), and ribonucleic acid (RNA) is found both in cell nuclei and cytoplasm. Nucleoprotein is a macromolecule composed of nucleic acid and protein.

Nucleolus (pl. *nucleoli*). A deep-staining, spherical body found inside the nuclear membrane.

Nucleus. A spherical-to-fusiform protoplasmic body found in the cytoplasm of most living cells and thought to be the metabolic center of the cell.

Nut. A dry, indehiscent, one-seeded fruit derived from a compound ovary in which the pericarp becomes very hard and stony.

Opposite leaf arrangement. Two leaves and/or two buds at a single node.

Osmosis. Diffusion of solvent (water) molecules in response to a free-energy gradient of these molecules through a differentially permeable membrane that allows more rapid passage of solvent than solute molecules.

Osmotic potential. A property of a solution, expressed in pressure terms, equivalent to the pressure that might be developed if the solution were placed in a perfect osmometer in contact with pure water at 1 atmosphere pressure.

Ovary. The fertile portion of the carpel or pistil.

Ovule. The structure occurring inside of the ovary and consisting of the embryo sac, the nucellus, and the integuments.

Palisade parenchyma. In leaves, columnar parenchyma cells found immediately under the upper epidermis.

Parallel venation. Leaf venation in which the major veins (vascular bundles) are parallel with one another.

Parenchyma. A tissue made up of thin-walled, usually isodiametric cells, which most often function as living elements.

Parthenocarpy. Development of a fruit without fertilization of the egg nucleus.

Pedicel. The stock of an individual flower in an inflorescence.

Peduncle. In those plants that bear only one flower, the peduncle is the flower stock.

Pepo. A special type of berry (such as cucumber) in which the exocarp forms a tough, leathery rind, the mesocarp and endocarp becoming fleshy and succulent.

Perianth. The calyx and corolla of a flower.

Pericarp. The entire ovary wall.

Periclinal. Parallel with the surface of the tissue or organ in question.

Pericycle. The outermost layer of the stele; in roots, the tissue immediately inside the endodermis and outside the primary vascular tissues.

Periderm. The cork, cork cambium, and phelloderm, collectively.

Perigynous. A floral condition in which the perianth parts and the androecium are located around the ovary.

Permeability. The extent to which a substance (such as a membrane) will allow another substance to pass through.

Petal. One of the leaf-like appendages making up the corolla.

Petiole. The stem-like part of the leaf.

Phelloderm. Parenchyma-like tissue produced on the inner surface of the cork cambium.

Phloem. The conducting tissue concerned primarily with the movement of elaborated food materials in the plant body; it is made up (in angiosperms) of sieve-tube elements, companion cells, parenchyma cells, and fibers.

Photon. A unit of light energy that cannot be further subdivided (a quantum of light energy). The shorter the wave length, the more energy per photon. (Energy per photon increases from infrared to red, green, blue, ultraviolet, X-rays, and cosmic rays.)

Photoperiodism. Growth, development, and flowering of plants in response to the length of day or night.

Photosynthesis. The conversion—in the presence of chlorophyll and other substances—of light energy, carbon dioxide, water, and certain minerals (such as nitrogen) to carbohydrates, amino acids, and perhaps other materials.

Phototropism. Growth of plant parts toward (positive, as in stems) or away from (negative, as in roots) a source of light.

Phytochrome. A proteinaceous plant pigment that appears to be in control of many plant-growth processes responding to light; characterized by a given response to orange-red light which may be subsequently reversed by far-red light (or *vice versa*).

Pistil, compound. A pistil composed of two or more united carpels or two or more united, simple pistils.

Pistil, simple. A pistil consisting of a single carpel.

Pith. The center of most stems and some roots, composed primarily of parenchyma tissue.

Placenta. The region or tissue in the ovary to which the funiculus is attached.

Plageotropic. Tending to grow horizontally.

Plasma membrane (or *plasmalemma*). The outer, limiting layer of the cytoplasm.

Plasmodesma. A cytoplasmic strand connecting two adjacent cells.

Plastid. A specialized cytoplasmic body concerned with photosynthesis and/or storage of various foods.

Plate meristem. A group of cells dividing in two planes only.

Plumule. That part of the embryo axis of the seed that will produce the shoot system.

Polar nuclei. Two nuclei usually located in the center of the mature embryo sac.

Pollen grain. The microspore or, more commonly, the male gametophyte plant in angiosperms that gives rise to the male gametes.

Pollen mother cells. The diploid cells in the anther which undergo meiosis, producing haploid microspores.

Pollen sac. The chamber in the anther where the pollen grains are located.

Pollen tube. A tube formed by the germinating pollen grain.

Pollination. The actual transfer of pollen grains from the anther of the stamen to the stigma of the carpel.

Pome. A fleshy accessory fruit, such as an apple.

Primary endosperm cell. The fusion product between a single sperm nucleus and two polar nuclei.

Primary root. The root that develops directly from the radicle of the embryo.

Primary tissue. Tissue that has its origin in the apical meristems of the plant.

Primary wall. The first wall layer formed inside the middle lamella by a growing or elongating cell.

Procambium. The primary meristematic tissue that gives rise to the primary vascular tissues of the plant body.

Protoderm. The primary meristematic tissue that gives rise to the epidermis of the plant body.

Protoplasm. The generalized, living substance composed of cytoplasm, nuclei, etc.

Quantum. A unit of energy that cannot be further subdivided. See *photon*.

Quiescence. The condition of a seed before it germinates—its failure to germinate usually being due to unsuitable temperature or moisture conditions.

Radicle. The embryonic, primary root of the seed.

Raphe. A ridge along one side of the seed coat, marking a region of fusion between the seed coat and the funiculus.

Ray initials. Cells in the vascular cambium that give rise to the vascular-ray tissue.

Receptacle. The terminal part of the pedicel or peduncle, to which are attached the various parts of the flower.

Relative humidity. The amount of moisture contained in vapor form in the air compared to the amount that the air could hold at any given temperature.

Respiration. Chemical, oxidative processes in which certain organic substances are broken down by protoplasm with the release of energy, some of which is used in growth and other functions.

Rhizoids. Unicellular or multicellular filamentous structures that serve as organelles of anchorage and absorption.

Rhizome. An underground stem, usually horizontally oriented and sometimes specialized for food storage.

Ribonucleic acid (RNA). A complex molecule occurring in both the cytoplasm and the nucleus. Plays an important role in synthesis of protein.

Root. The multicellular, subterranean plant organ; composed of several tissue systems, vertically and/or horizontally oriented; concerned with absorption, anchorage, etc.

Root cap. Protective tissue surrounding and enclosing the root apical meristem.

Root hair. An elongate extension of a root epidermal cell, specialized as an absorbing structure.

Root pressure. Pressure in the xylem system developed by the root through active absorption.

Samara. A dry, indehiscent, one-seeded fruit in which the seed coat is extended to form a wing.

Sapwood. The secondary xylem that is still active and contains some living cells.

Scalariform. Ladder-like, used with reference to thickenings in tracheary elements and also to arrangement of pits in secondary cell walls.

Scarification. The process of overcoming the dormancy of certain seeds by breaking the seed coat.

Sclereids. More or less isodiametric cells with thick, lignified, secondary walls functioning as dead elements.

Sclerenchyma. A generalized term for strengthening or mechanical tissue, made up usually of two types of cells separated from each other on the basis of length, elongated fibers, and more or less isodiametric sclereids. These cells differ from collenchyma in that they function as dead elements and have thick, lignified secondary walls.

Scutellum. The specialized cotyledon of members of the grass family.

Secondary tissue. Tissue derived from a lateral meristem.

Semipermeable. Technically, a property of a membrane through which certain substances pass while others do not; more practically, a property through which certain substances pass more rapidly than others.

Senescence phase. That phase of growth in which growth rate (increment of growth per unit time interval) decreases with time.

Sepals. The outermost, sterile, leaf-like parts of a complete flower.

Sessile. Applied to leaves that lack a petiole.

Shoot system. The stems and leaves of any given plant.

Sieve-tube elements. The phloem cells that perform the function of food conduction; characterized by having sieve-like areas on the end walls and side walls.

Silique. A dry, dehiscent fruit characteristic of the family *Cruciferae* (the mustard family).

Simple perforation plate. The end wall of a vessel element with only a single large perforation or hole.

Softwood. A general term for the secondary xylem of coniferous species (pines, spruces, firs, etc.).

Solutes. Substances (usually ions or molecules) dissolved in a solvent.

Solution. A solvent containing molecules or ions of one or more solutes homogeneously dispersed in it.

Solvent. A substance that contains certain solutes in solution.

Sorus (pl. *sori*). A group of sporangia on the sporophylls of ferns.

Species. A group of closely similar individuals usually interbreeding freely; the unit of classification next below the genus.

Spectrum. A series of radiations arranged in the order of wave length (for example, the visible spectrum).

Sperm. The male gamete.

Sperm nuclei. The male gametes of angiosperms; formed in the pollen tube, usually by a mitotic division of the generative nucleus.

Spongy parenchyma. The loosely packed, more or less isodiametric tissue in dicotyledonous leaves immediately above the lower epidermis.

Sporangiophore. A structure that bears one or more sporangia.

Sporangium. A case or structure in which spores are formed.

Spores. Asexual reproduction structures borne in sporangia, often having thick walls and limited reserve food material.

Sporophyll. A fertile leaf or a leaf that bears sporangia.

Sporophyte. The diploid, spore-producing plant that arises from the embryo or the zygote.

Springwood. The first-formed xylem of the annual ring.

Stamen. An individual unit of the male part of the flower; the part of the flower that produces pollen.

Staminate. A flower or a plant that bears only stamens; carpels are absent.

Stele. In roots, and rarely in stems, the pericycle and all tissues inside this cell layer.

Stigma. The pollen-receptive, terminal part of the carpel.

Stimulus. Any environmental change that activates a receptor.

Stomate (stoma) (pl. *stomata*). A pore or opening between two guard cells.

Stratification. A process used to break the dormancy of certain seeds by exposing them in the moist condition to temperatures near freezing for an extended period of time.

Strobilus. A cone.

Style. The elongated, sterile portion of the carpel positioned between the stigma and the ovary.

Suberin. A fatty, waxy material found in the walls of cork cells and in the Casparian strip of endodermal cells.

Succulent. A plant, such as cactus, that accumulates reserves of water in fleshy stems, leaves, or roots.

Summerwood. The later-formed, secondary xylem in any given annual ring.

Swimming sperm. A motile sperm cell with flagella.

Symbiosis. An intimate association between two different kinds of organisms. In the most common usage of the word, both organisms are mutually benefited.

Symplast. The system of interconnected protoplasm (through plasmodesmata in the cell walls) in the plant.

Synergids. The two cells flanking the egg in the mature embryo sac.

Synergism. A kind of response to two chemical substances (e.g., growth regulators) in which the combined response is greater than the sum of the responses to each substance applied alone.

Taproot system. A root system consisting of one large, vertically oriented root bearing many smaller laterals.

Taxon. A unit of taxonomic classification such as family, genus, or species.

Taxonomy. The branch of botany that deals with the classification of plants.

Thallus. A complete plant body lacking a conductive system such as that found in true roots, stems, or leaves; a simple, unspecialized plant body.

Thermoperiodism. A positive plant response to differences in day and night temperature.

Tissue culture. The cultivation under sterile conditions of pieces of tissue or organs on an artificial medium.

Tonoplast. The vacuolar membrane.

Totipotent. Having the ability, as in a cell, to regenerate an entire plant body.

Tracheid. Elongated, unicellular, conducting cell found in the xylem of vascular plants; functions as a dead element, has lignified secondary walls.

Translocation. The movement of dissolved substances within plants; usually movement of organic substances in the phloem.

Transpiration. The evaporation of water from plants.

Triploid nuclei. Nuclei with three sets (triploid) of chromosomes.

Tube nucleus. In the germinated pollen grain, the nucleus found in the end of the pollen tube.

Tunica. In apical meristems, the outer cell layer(s), in which all division is limited to the anticlinal plane.

Vacuolar membrane. The tonoplast or cytoplasmic membrane surrounding and enclosing the vacuole.

Vacuole. A nonliving space or cavity in the protoplasm filled with a water solution.

Vascular bundles. A coherent group of vascular cells; that is, xylem and phloem, plus, in some cases, associated mechanical tissue.

Vascular cambium. The lateral meristem that produces secondary xylem and secondary phloem.

Veins. An individual vascular bundle in the leaf.

Vernalization. The induction of flowering in a plant through the exposure of the seed or later growth stages to low temperatures (usually a few degrees above freezing).

Vessel element. One of the cells that make up the vessel—a multicellular water-conducting structure in the xylem of angiosperms.

Viable. Alive; the ability to germinate and grow, as applied to seeds.

Whorled leaf arrangement. Three or more leaves attached to a stem at a single node.

Wood. Secondary xylem derived from the vascular cambium.

Wound hormone. A substance produced by the injured plant tissue which stimulates cell division a few layers of cells below the wound.

Xylem. A complex tissue made up (in the angiosperms) of four cell types: fibers, tracheids, vessel elements, and parenchyma, and performing the primary function of water conduction in the plant body.

Xylem rays. Horizontally oriented aggregations of parenchyma cells (and sometimes tracheids also) in the xylem.

Zygote. The diploid cell that is produced by fusion of egg and sperm.

INDEX